MATH TRAILBLAZERS™

Grade
4

Unit Resource Guide
Unit 9
Shapes and Solids

SECOND EDITION

A Mathematical Journey Using Science and Language Arts

KENDALL/HUNT PUBLISHING COMPANY
4050 Westmark Drive   Dubuque, Iowa 52002

A TIMS® Curriculum
University of Illinois at Chicago

UIC The University of Illinois
at Chicago

The original edition was based on work supported by the National Science Foundation under grant No. MDR 9050226 and the University of Illinois at Chicago. Any opinions, findings, and conclusions or recommendations expressed in this publication are those of the author(s) and do not necessarily reflect the views of the granting agencies.

Printed in the United States of America

1   2   3   4   5   6   7   8   9   10   07   06   05   04   03

LETTER HOME
Shapes and Solids

Date: _____

Dear Family Member:

This unit continues our exploration of geometry. Children first review what an angle is and then learn how to measure angles with a protractor.

Angles play an important role in symmetry. In this unit, children explore turn symmetry and line symmetry. The study of symmetry gives names to patterns that children see in everyday life—for example, designs in architecture or flower petals.

Your child will need some empty boxes (cereal boxes work well). We will use these boxes to analyze three-dimensional objects and learn about volume. By cutting the boxes into rectangles, children learn how two-dimensional figures come together to make three-dimensional objects. This is important for the development of spatial visualization.

This unit continues the yearlong study of the division facts. Your child will review and work toward gaining fluency with the division facts for the fives and tens. Help your child review these facts with the *Triangle Flash Cards*. Your child will bring these cards home to study.

Thank you for your continued interest in your child's mathematical explorations.

Sincerely,

_____

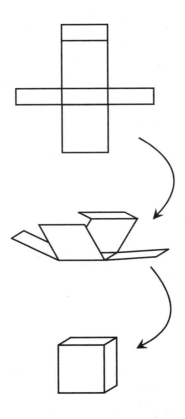

Students learn how two-dimensional figures become three-dimensional objects.

UNIT 9 — UNIT OUTLINE

Shapes and Solids

Pacing Suggestions

- The Daily Practice and Problems continues the practice and assessment of the division facts begun in Unit 8 Lesson 8. In Unit 9 students practice the first group of facts, the fives and tens. Allow time for students to practice, share strategies, and use them to solve problems. Students continue to practice small groups of facts throughout Units 10–16. They take an inventory test of all the division facts in Unit 16. This work with the division facts is also found in the *Grade 4 Facts Resource Guide.* Use this guide if your pacing schedule is significantly different from the recommended schedule.

- Lessons 4 and 7 are optional lessons. Both lessons extend concepts and make connections to other subject areas. Lesson 4 *Journey to Flatopia* connects math and language arts in an *Adventure Book* story. Lesson 7 *Building an Octahedron* makes connections to art. Students can make use of language arts and art time to complete these lessons.

Components Key: SG = Student Guide, DAB = Discovery Assignment Book, AB = Adventure Book, URG = Unit Resource Guide, and DPP = Daily Practice and Problems

	Sessions	Description	Supplies
LESSON 1 **Lines** SG pages 238–242 URG pages 26–34 DPP A–B	1–2	**ACTIVITY:** Students learn about points, lines, line segments, and rays. They investigate parallel lines.	• rulers
LESSON 2 **What's Your Angle?** SG pages 243–250 DAB pages 127–129 URG pages 35–48 DPP C–F	2	**ACTIVITY:** Students learn to measure angles with a protractor and draw angles. Lines, line segments, rays, and points are discussed. **ASSESSMENT PAGE:** *Measuring Angles II,* Discovery Assignment Book, page 129.	• protractors • cardboard corner or plastic right triangle
LESSON 3 **Symmetry** SG pages 251–255 DAB pages 131–139 URG pages 49–62 DPP G–J	2	**ACTIVITY:** Students investigate turning (rotational) and line (reflective) symmetry.	• protractors • rulers • pattern blocks • scissors • calculators • blank paper • construction paper

	Sessions	Description	Supplies
LESSON 4		*– OPTIONAL LESSON –*	
Journey to Flatopia AB pages 29–44 URG pages 63–70	1	**ADVENTURE BOOK:** Students explore two- and three-dimensional worlds in a story about travel through the fourth dimension.	
LESSON 5			
Prisms SG pages 256–262 DAB pages 141–149 URG pages 71–85 DPP K–N	2–3	**ACTIVITY:** Students learn about rectangular prisms by cutting them to form nets. Students explore nets of various prisms and build their own prisms.	• rulers • cereal boxes • transparent tape • scissors • protractors • other rectangular boxes
LESSON 6			
Finding the Volume of a Prism SG pages 263–267 URG pages 86–96 DPP O–R	2–3	**ACTIVITY:** Students find the volumes of various prisms.	• centimeter connecting cubes • geometric solids or prisms • calculators • base-ten pack • base-ten flats • juice packs
LESSON 7		*– OPTIONAL LESSON –*	
Building an Octahedron DAB page 151 URG pages 97–99	1	**OPTIONAL ACTIVITY:** Students construct an octahedron and discuss the mathematics they see.	• scissors • tape
LESSON 8			
Constructing a Prism URG pages 100–106 DPP S–V	2	**ASSESSMENT ACTIVITY:** Students design a net for a triangular prism and answer questions about symmetry, angles, and volume. **ASSESSMENT PAGE:** *Constructing a Prism,* Unit Resource Guide, page 105.	• protractors • rulers • scissors • tape • calculators

CONNECTIONS

A current list of connections is available at www.mathtrailblazers.com.

Software **Suggested Titles**

- *Building Perspective* develops spatial reasoning and visual thinking in three dimensions.
- *Carmen Sandiego Math Detective* provides practice with math facts, estimation, ordering numbers, and word problems.
- *The Factory Deluxe* promotes spatial reasoning and practices finding area.
- *Logo* is a drawing program that helps students develop spatial reasoning and an understanding of coordinates while making shapes.
- *Math Arena* is a collection of math activities that reinforces many math concepts.
- *Math Workshop Deluxe* develops spatial sense and math facts proficiency.
- *Mighty Math Calculating Crew* poses short answer questions about three-dimensional shapes.
- *Mighty Math Number Heroes* poses short answer questions about polygons.
- *National Library of Virtual Manipulatives* website (http://matti.usu.edu) allows students to work with manipulatives including geoboards and tangrams.
- *Shape Up!* is a geometry program that contains five sets of shapes that students can manipulate and explore.
- *Tessellation Exploration* develops understanding of the geometry of tessellations and allows students to create their own.
- *TesselMania Deluxe!* provides opportunities to design tessellations and develop an understanding of the geometry involved in tessellations.

PREPARING FOR UPCOMING LESSONS

Collect boxes and prisms with different bases. See Before the Activity in Lessons 5 and 6. Arrange for students to bring juice boxes, one per student group, for Lesson 6. Students will measure the volume of the box in Lesson 6.

In Unit 10, students will participate in an experiment called *Downhill Racer*. Ask students to bring in toy cars, skates, or other vehicles that roll well for this lab.

Shapes and Solids

The theme of this unit is representing and describing shapes in two and three dimensions. We start with lessons reviewing some of the basic ideas of two-dimensional geometry—lines and angles.

Lines

The concept of **line** is fundamental to geometry. When we say "line" in mathematics, we always mean "straight line." There are several ways to describe the notion of a line mathematically. However, we want to keep our approach to geometry at an intuitive, common-sense level. The basic tool we use for drawing a line is a straightedge. Since the edge of a ruler is straight, a figure carefully drawn to be alongside the edge of the ruler will represent a line. Another way to "construct" a straight line is to fold a piece of paper. Finally, you may recall the definition of a line as "the shortest distance between two points." This means that a rubber band stretched between two points will run along a straight line. The nice thing about this last approach is that it works in three-dimensional space as well as in the two-dimensional plane.

Angles

Angles have been discussed and used throughout the curriculum. In this unit, the intuitive idea of angle is developed further. One reason the concept of angle is important is that the angle between two lines describes the way that the two lines meet. For example, two lines are perpendicular if they meet at a 90-degree angle. Although this is a seemingly simple concept, children often have misconceptions about angles. For example, students often believe that the size of an angle depends on the length of the sides of the angle (Wilson and Osborne, 1988). Other studies show that students sometimes believe that right angles are angles that open to the right (Crowley, 1987). This is another example of students confusing mathematical language (in which right angle means 90-degree angle) and everyday language (in which right is a direction opposite to left). To avoid such misconceptions, children must see angles drawn in different positions and with sides of different lengths.

In this unit children compare angles, as they did in Unit 2. The exercises here review that the important

characteristic of the angle is the size of the opening. Many researchers believe that comparison is an important first step in understanding a new measurement system (Wilson and Osborne, 1988). The lesson then continues with children learning to use a protractor to measure angles.

Symmetry

Symmetry is revisited in this unit. While many elementary students are familiar with line (reflective) symmetry, many are not aware that there are three types of symmetry in the plane:

Line (reflective) symmetry

Turn (rotational) symmetry

Translational symmetry

Figures that have **turn symmetry** have a center of turning and an angle of turning. Often, these are referred to as the center of rotation and the angle of rotation. The **angle of turning** is the smallest angle through which the figure can be turned about the center of turning so that the figure coincides with itself. In Figure 1, the shape repeats itself six times so the angle of turning is 360 degrees/6 = 60 degrees. We say this figure has $\frac{1}{6}$-turn symmetry. Other authors refer to this as sixfold symmetry.

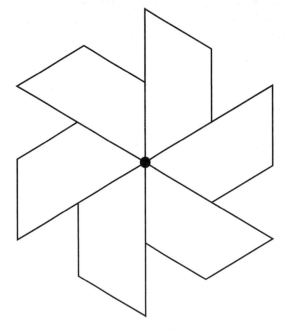

Figure 1: *A shape with $\frac{1}{6}$-turn symmetry*

A figure that has **line symmetry** has at least one **line of symmetry.** If the figure is folded along this line, the two pieces will match exactly. Some figures have more than one line of symmetry, as shown in Figure 2.

Often, figures that have turn symmetry have line symmetry as well. For example, Figure 2 has two lines of symmetry and $\frac{1}{2}$-turn symmetry.

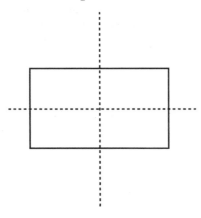

Figure 2: *A rectangle with two lines of symmetry*

The third type of symmetry is called translational. A figure with **translational symmetry** is often referred to as a repeating pattern. In other words, a certain part of the figure, the pattern, is repeated over and over by sliding it repeatedly a fixed distance. An example is shown in Figure 3. This unit focuses on rotational and line symmetry.

Figure 3: *A shape with translational symmetry*

Investigating symmetries helps students analyze the shapes they encounter as they study geometry. This will aid them in their development of geometric thinking (Crowley, 1987). The study of symmetry gives names to patterns they see in everyday life and in art. For example, we can see patterns of symmetry in architecture as well as in the petals of many flowers. Students who have been introduced to these notions will be better able to analyze and describe what they see.

Three-Dimensional Shapes

Another focus of this unit is the study of three-dimensional shapes and the ways we can build three-dimensional shapes from two-dimensional shapes. Three-dimensional objects are often called **solids.** In Lesson 5, students cut cereal boxes along their edges to flatten them out. The pattern of the flattened cereal box is called a **net.** Nets are explored to help develop students' spatial visualization. In particular, we give students nets for various shapes and have them build three-dimensional shapes by cutting and pasting. In order to do this, students need to visualize the three-dimensional figure by looking at the two-dimensional net. Visual imagery is important in the development of mathematical thinking and can be improved by exercises such as these (Fuys and Liebov, 1993).

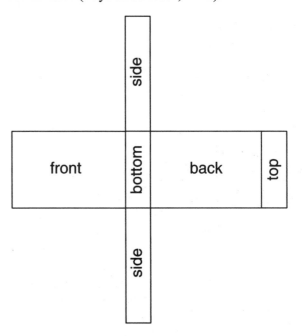

Figure 4: *A net of a cereal box*

Students then build solids from nets. (Technically, the objects students build from nets are the surface of a solid. However, we often use the same term to refer to a solid and the surface of a solid. Most of the three-dimensional shapes your students will build will be prisms. Figure 5 shows some examples. **Prisms** are solids with two identical polygonal faces that are often referred to as bases. The sides of prisms are parallelograms. In this unit we deal with only right prisms, so the sides are rectangles.

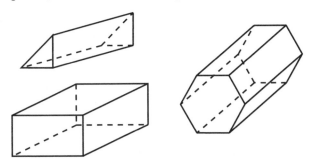

Figure 5: *Examples of right prisms*

Students will find the volumes of some prisms. Your students have a good deal of previous experience with volume. In earlier grades, students built prisms from centimeter cubes and explored the relationship between the volume of a prism and its height. They also explored volume as measured by displacement. In this unit, a slightly different approach is taken. Given a rectangular prism, students must envision how many centimeter cubes it would take to fill the shape, knowing the area of the base and height of the prism. Experiencing all these different approaches helps students develop a solid understanding of volume. For more information on volume, see the TIMS Tutor: *Volume* in the *Teacher Implementation Guide.*

Students can also build an octahedron in Lesson 7. See Figure 6. Although this lesson is optional, students can enjoy constructing and decorating these shapes. The octahedron lesson can also be done any time during the year and coordinated with art class. Experiences such as these reinforce the strong relationship between mathematics and art and develop an appreciation for both disciplines.

Figure 6: *An octahedron*

Resources

- Crowley, Mary L. "The van Hiele Model of the Development of Geometric Thought." *Learning and Teaching Geometry, K–12. 1987 Yearbook.* Mary Montgomery Lindquist (ed.). National Council of Teachers of Mathematics, Reston, VA, 1987.

- Fuys, David J., and Amy K. Liebov. "Geometry and Spatial Sense." *Research Ideas for the Classroom, Early Childhood Mathematics.* Robert J. Jensen (ed.). Macmillan Publishing Company, New York, 1993.

- Wilson, Patricia R., and Alan Osborne. "Foundational Ideas in Teaching about Measure." *Teaching Mathematics in Grades K–8, Research-Based Methods.* Thomas R. Post (ed.). Allyn and Bacon, Inc., Boston, 1988.

Assessment Indicators

- Can students measure angles?
- Can students identify acute, obtuse, and right angles?
- Can students identify line and turn symmetry?
- Can students describe 2- and 3-dimensional shapes using their properties?
- Can students identify a net of a prism?
- Can students find the volume of a rectangular prism?
- Do students demonstrate fluency with the division facts for the 5s and 10s?

OBSERVATIONAL ASSESSMENT RECORD

(A1) Can students measure angles?

(A2) Can students identify acute, obtuse, and right angles?

(A3) Can students identify line and turn symmetry?

(A4) Can students describe 2- and 3-dimensional shapes using their properties?

(A5) Can students identify a net of a prism?

(A6) Can students find the volume of a rectangular prism?

(A7) Do students demonstrate fluency with the division facts for the 5s and 10s?

(A8) _____

Name	A1	A2	A3	A4	A5	A6	A7	A8	Comments
1.									
2.									
3.									
4.									
5.									
6.									
7.									
8.									
9.									
10.									
11.									
12.									
13.									

Name	A1	A2	A3	A4	A5	A6	A7	A8	Comments
14.									
15.									
16.									
17.									
18.									
19.									
20.									
21.									
22.									
23.									
24.									
25.									
26.									
27.									
28.									
29.									
30.									
31.									
32.									

Daily Practice and Problems

Shapes and Solids

Two Daily Practice and Problems (DPP) items are included for each class session listed in the Unit Outline. The first item is always a Bit and the second is either a Task or a Challenge. Refer to the Daily Practice and Problems and Home Practice Guide in the *Teacher Implementation Guide* for further information on the DPP. A Scope and Sequence Chart for the DPP can be found in the Scope and Sequence Chart & the NCTM *Principles and Standards* section of the *Teacher Implementation Guide*.

A DPP Menu for Unit 9

Eight icons designate the subject matter of the DPP items. Each DPP item falls into one or more of the categories listed below. A brief menu of the DPP items included in Unit 9 follows.

N **Number Sense** D, F, G, O, V	✖ **Computation** D, G, O, Q, S	◔ **Time** T	◈ **Geometry** A, I, J, N, P
⁵ₓ₇ **Math Facts** B, C, E, K, M, O, R, U, V	$ **Money** F	⚖ **Measurement** A, J, Q	▱ **Data** H, L

Practicing and Assessing the Division Facts

In Units 3–8, DPP items reviewed the multiplication facts and helped students develop strategies for learning the division facts. In Units 9–16, students will concentrate on gaining fluency with the division facts. Our goal is for students to achieve fluency with the division facts by the end of the year.

In Unit 8 Lesson 8, students learned how to use *Triangle Flash Cards* to quiz themselves on the division facts and learned to use the *Division Facts I Know* charts to record their progress with the division facts. They began with the first group of facts, the fives and tens.

The main strategy for learning the division facts is to use the related multiplication facts. Therefore, expectations for fluency with the division facts have been delayed until children have reasonable fluency with the multiplication facts. In the first semester of fourth grade, we began using fact families in the DPP to connect students' knowledge of the multiplication facts to learning the division facts.

Throughout Units 9–16, students will practice the division facts to develop fluency. In fifth grade, students use fact families to review the multiplication and division facts. For more information about

the distribution and assessment of the math facts throughout the curriculum, see the TIMS Tutor: *Math Facts* in the *Teacher Implementation Guide*. Also refer to the DPP guide in the *Unit Resource Guide* for Unit 3 and the *Grade 4 Facts Resource Guide*.

As in the first semester, students use the flash cards to assess themselves on their progress with the facts. Students sort the cards into three piles—those they know well and can answer quickly, those they know using a strategy, and those they need to learn. Students circle the facts for which they have demonstrated fluency—those that they know well and can answer quickly—on their *Division Facts I Know* charts. Special emphasis should be placed on the other two piles—those facts they know using a strategy and those they need to learn. Discuss strategies students may use to solve the facts quickly, emphasizing those strategies that are more efficient than others. Using more efficient strategies should result in fluency.

Aside from sorting the *Triangle Flash Cards,* students practice their facts in other Bits and Tasks throughout the DPP in Units 9–16. Then, at the end of each unit, students take a quiz on the groups of facts highlighted in that unit. By continually updating their *Division Facts I Know* charts after sorting flash cards and taking quizzes, students can see for themselves which facts they have learned and which facts they need to practice.

Part 1 of the Home Practice for Units 9–13 reminds students to take home their flash cards to practice. The *Triangle Flash Cards: 5s* and *10s* are located in the *Discovery Assignment Book* in Unit 8 Lesson 8. The remaining groups of flash cards are located after the Home Practice in Units 10–13. The flash cards are also in the Generic Section. The table below outlines the distribution of division facts practice and assessment throughout the DPP. In Unit 16, an inventory test of the division facts is administered as part of the DPP.

Unit	Triangle Flash Cards: Group Organized by Strategy	Division Facts Assessment
8	5s and 10s	• Sort flash cards and begin *Division Facts I Know* charts
9	5s and 10s	• Quiz and update charts
10	2s and 3s	• Sort flash cards and update charts • Quiz and update charts
11	square numbers	• Sort flash cards and update charts • Quiz and update charts
12	9s	• Sort flash cards and update charts • Quiz and update charts
13	the last six facts	• Sort flash cards and update charts • Quiz and update charts
14	5s, 10s, 2s, and square numbers	• Sort flash cards and update charts • Quiz and update charts
15	3s, 9s, last six facts	• Sort flash cards and update charts • Quiz and update charts
16	all five groups	• Inventory test on all five groups

Daily Practice and Problems

Students may solve the items individually, in groups, or as a class. The items may also be assigned for homework.

Student Questions	Teacher Notes

A Angles

Use 90° and 180° as benchmarks to draw the following angles.

1. Sketch an angle that is about 95°. Tell if your angle is acute, right, or obtuse.

2. Sketch an angle that is about 45°. Tell if your angle is acute, right, or obtuse.

3. Sketch an angle that is about 120°. Tell if your angle is acute, right, or obtuse.

TIMS Bit

Sketches will vary. One possible sketch is shown for each.

1. Obtuse

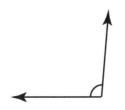

2. Acute

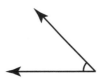

3. Obtuse

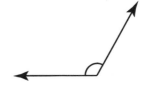

Student Questions	Teacher Notes

 Fact Families for × and ÷

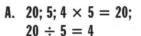

TIMS Task

The following four facts are in the same fact family:

$7 \times 10 = 70$ $10 \times 7 = 70$

$70 \div 7 = 10$ $70 \div 10 = 7$

Solve each pair of related number sentences.

Then, give two other facts that are in the same fact family.

A. $5 \times 4 = ?$ and $20 \div 4 = ?$

B. $3 \times 10 = ?$ and $30 \div 3 = ?$

C. $10 \times 5 = ?$ and $50 \div 10 = ?$

D. $8 \times 5 = ?$ and $40 \div 5 = ?$

E. $6 \times 10 = ?$ and $60 \div 6 = ?$

F. $10 \times 8 = ?$ and $80 \div 8 = ?$

A. 20; 5; $4 \times 5 = 20$; $20 \div 5 = 4$

B. 30; 10; $10 \times 3 = 30$; $30 \div 10 = 3$

C. 50; 5; $5 \times 10 = 50$; $50 \div 5 = 10$

D. 40; 8; $5 \times 8 = 40$; $40 \div 8 = 5$

E. 60; 10; $10 \times 6 = 60$; $60 \div 10 = 6$

F. 80; 10; $8 \times 10 = 80$; $80 \div 10 = 8$

C **Practicing the Facts**

TIMS Bit

A. $5 \div 1 =$ B. $40 \div 4 =$

C. $15 \div 3 =$ D. $100 \div 10 =$

E. $45 \div 5 =$ F. $25 \div 5 =$

G. $60 \div 10 =$ H. $35 \div 7 =$

I. $10 \div 5 =$ J. $30 \div 5 =$

K. $0 \div 5 =$

A. 5

B. 10

C. 5

D. 10

E. 9

F. 5

G. 6

H. 5

I. 2

J. 6

K. 0

Student Questions	Teacher Notes

 Multiplication Practice

Solve the following problems using paper and pencil. Estimate to make sure your answers are reasonable.

1. A. $48 \times 5 =$ B. $88 \times 8 =$

   C. $65 \times 5 =$ D. $54 \times 4 =$

   E. $27 \times 5 =$ F. $74 \times 7 =$

2. Explain your estimation strategy for Question 1C.

TIMS Task

1. A. 240   B. 704

   C. 325   D. 216

   E. 135   F. 518

2. Strategies will vary. Possible strategy: since $60 \times 5 = 300$ and $70 \times 5 = 350$, then the answer is between 300 and 350.

 Division Stories

The following two problems can be solved using division.

1. Mrs. Randall gave each of her children $4 to spend on games at the neighborhood carnival. If Mrs. Randall gave out $20 in all, how many children does she have? Draw a picture to show this problem.

2. One package of bus tokens contains 10 tokens. Keenya's mother needs 40 tokens to get to and from work for one month. How many packages does Keenya's mother need? Draw a picture to show this problem.

TIMS Bit

Pictures will vary, but the important idea here is that division is used to sort and organize larger numbers into smaller, even groups of numbers.

1. $20 in all ÷ $4 to each child = 5 children

2. 40 tokens ÷ 10 tokens per package = 4 packages

F Money

1. What coins can be used to make 16 cents? How many different ways can you answer this?

2. What is the least number of coins you can use to make 35 cents? Tell which coins.

3. What is the greatest number of coins you can use to make 40 cents? Tell which coins.

TIMS Task

1. There are 6 ways.

Dimes	Nickels	Pennies
1	1	1
1		6
	3	1
	2	6
	1	11
		16

2. 2 coins; 1 quarter and 1 dime

3. 40 pennies

G Mental Math

Do the following problems in your head.

A. $850 - 200 =$ B. $780 + 20 =$

C. $1250 + 125 =$ D. $379 - 80 =$

E. $398 + 103 =$ F. $8000 - 4500 =$

TIMS Bit

Encourage students to share their strategies. To solve D, for example, one might subtract 79 first to get 300. Then, subtract 1 more to get 299.

A. 650   B. 800

C. 1375   D. 299

E. 501   F. 3500

Student Questions	Teacher Notes

 Whose Is Whose?

After gym class, Ms. Lyons asked Maya, Irma, and Linda to check the lost and found. They found a green glove, baseball hat, and jacket. Each girl had lost one item.

Use the clues below to determine who lost which item.

Clue A: Irma and Linda went to the lost and found together. One of them claimed the baseball hat and the other claimed the green glove.

Clue B: The green glove was not Irma's.

TIMS Task

This is the first of a series of logic puzzles which will appear throughout the DPP in succeeding units. The difficulty of the puzzles will gradually increase. Solution strategies will be discussed in the Teacher Notes. Allow students to try solving this problem in pairs or in groups of three.

Since Irma did not own the glove, Linda owned the green glove. Therefore, the baseball hat was Irma's. The jacket must be Maya's.

 Geometric Gems

Find and name at least one of each of the following:

1. an acute angle

2. an obtuse angle

3. a triangle

4. a quadrilateral

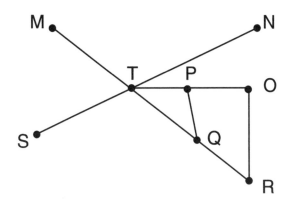

TIMS Bit

Accept all possible answers.

1. Possible answers are:
   ∠NTP, ∠PTQ, ∠MTS, ∠TQP, ∠TRO, ∠NTR

2. ∠MTN, ∠PQR, ∠STR, ∠TPQ, ∠MTO, ∠STO

3. △TPQ, △TOR

4. PQRO

J **Estimating Angles**

Refer to the drawing. Tell whether the given angle is acute, obtuse, right, or 180°. Estimate the size of the angle in degrees. Think of a right angle and a 180° angle as references.

Accept reasonable estimates.

1. ∠BED

2. ∠BEC

3. ∠AEB

4. ∠CED

5. ∠DEA

1. right, 90°

2. acute, 25°–40°

3. obtuse, 120°–150°

4. acute, 50°–70°

5. obtuse, 110°–120°

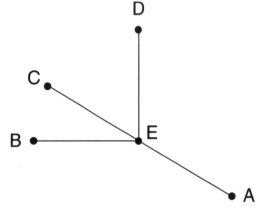

 K **More Fact Practice**

TIMS Bit

Find *n* to make each number sentence true.

A. $8 \times 5 = n$ B. $n \times 7 = 70$

C. $n \div 4 = 5$ D. $80 \div n = 10$

E. $10 \times n = 50$ F. $30 \div 5 = n$

G. $9 \times 10 = n$ H. $15 \div n = 5$

I. $n \times 8 = 80$ J. $10 \div 10 = n$

A. 40   B. 10

C. 20   D. 8

E. 5   F. 6

G. 90   H. 3

I. 10   J. 1

Which Is Which?

Nila, Grace, Tanya, and Lee Yah are in gymnastics class. Each girl is practicing on a different piece of equipment: balance beam, vault, trampoline, and uneven parallel bars.

Read the clues below to discover which girl is working on which piece of equipment.

Clue A: Nila and her friend who is on the balance beam are more advanced than Grace.

Clue B: Tanya and her friend who is on the trampoline are better at round-offs than Lee Yah and Grace.

Clue C: The girl on the vault and Grace both watched the Olympic gymnastic trials last Saturday on TV.

Clue D: Lee Yah is not on the balance beam.

TIMS Challenge

Encourage students to extract all information from each clue before moving to the next clue. They should keep track of all the "positive" and "negative" information. Encourage students to share their solution strategies. One group might jot down little notes after reading each clue. Another group might organize this information in a table like the following:

Name	Balance Beam	Vault	Trampo-line	Parallel Bars
Nila	no	no	yes	no
Grace	no	no	no	yes
Tanya	yes	no	no	no
Lee Yah	no	yes	no	no

To use the table, students mark a box with a "yes" when the information matches a person or piece of equipment. A box is marked "no" if a person or piece of equipment can be ruled out.

More Fact Families for × and ÷

TIMS Bit

New uniforms for the cheerleading and pompom squads were delivered today at Oakland High. Each box contained 8 uniforms. If 40 uniforms were ordered in all, how many boxes arrived?

There are 5 groups of 8 in 40. Think: $? \times 8 = 40$ or $40 \div 8 = ?$

The answer to both questions is 5.

Solve the following problems. Each group of facts is related.

A. $10 \times 7 =$ $70 \div 7 =$

    $7 \times 10 =$ $70 \div 10 =$

B. $2 \times 5 =$ $10 \div 5 =$

    $5 \times 2 =$ $10 \div 2 =$

C. $6 \times 5 =$ $30 \div 5 =$

    $5 \times 6 =$ $30 \div 6 =$

Among other strategies, students can use their knowledge of the multiplication facts to solve division facts. Encourage students to share their strategies.

A. 70; 10; 70; 7

B. 10; 2; 10; 5

C. 30; 6; 30; 5

Parallel and Perpendicular

1. Draw a line segment on your paper and label the endpoints A and B.

2. Draw a line segment parallel to $\overline{AB}$ and label it $\overline{CD}$.

3. Draw a line segment, $\overline{EF}$, perpendicular to $\overline{AB}$ and intersecting $\overline{AB}$ and $\overline{CD}$.

4. Is $\overline{EF}$ also perpendicular to $\overline{CD}$? Why or why not?

5. Draw another line segment that is neither perpendicular nor parallel to any of the others.

6. Carefully erase your letters and show your drawing to a friend. Have him or her show you a pair of parallel lines and a pair of perpendicular lines.

TIMS Challenge

Sample drawings will vary but should demonstrate parallelism and perpendicularity.

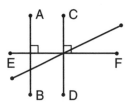

4. Yes, a line that is perpendicular to one line is also perpendicular to any line parallel to it.

Multiplying by Multiples of Ten

A. $8 \times 500 =$ B. $6 \times 100 =$

C. $2 \times 5000 =$ D. $5000 \times 6 =$

E. $50,000 \times 1 =$ F. $9 \times 50 =$

TIMS Bit

A. 4000
B. 600
C. 10,000
D. 30,000
E. 50,000
F. 450

Latvian Puzzle

1. Count the number of squares in the design.

2. Count the number of triangles in the design.

3. Draw as many lines of symmetry as you can in the design.

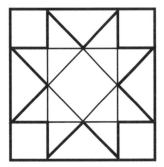

TIMS Challenge

1. There are 11 squares.

2. There are 40 triangles.

3. There are 4 lines of symmetry (Lines a, b, c, and d).

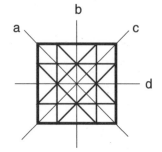

 Measuring Volume

Maya filled a 250-cc graduated cylinder with 140 cc of water. She added four marbles to the cylinder. The water level rose to 156 cc.

1. What is the total volume of the marbles?

2. What is the volume of one of the marbles?

3. Maya predicted that the total volume of the four marbles was 19 cc. Was her prediction within 10% of the actual volume of the four marbles?

TIMS Bit

1. 16 cc

2. 4 cc

3. Question 3 is for students who completed optional Lesson 5 in Unit 6.

No. 10% of 16 is between 1 and 2 cc. Maya's prediction was 3 cubic centimeters more than the actual.

Student Questions	Teacher Notes

 Even More Fact Families for × and ÷

The following four facts are in the same fact family:

$6 \times 5 = 30$ $5 \times 6 = 30$

$30 \div 5 = 6$ $30 \div 6 = 5$

Solve each pair of related number sentences.

Then, give two other facts that are in the same fact family.

A. $2 \times 10 = ?$ and $20 \div 10 = ?$

B. $3 \times 5 = ?$ and $15 \div 5 = ?$

C. $7 \times 5 = ?$ and $35 \div 7 = ?$

D. $10 \times 9 = ?$ and $90 \div 9 = ?$

E. $4 \times 10 = ?$ and $40 \div 10 = ?$

F. $5 \times 9 = ?$ and $45 \div 9 = ?$

TIMS Task

A. 20; 2; $10 \times 2 = 20$
and $20 \div 2 = 10$

B. 15; 3; $5 \times 3 = 15$
and $15 \div 3 = 5$

C. 35; 5; $5 \times 7 = 35$
and $35 \div 5 = 7$

D. 90; 10; $9 \times 10 = 90$
and $90 \div 10 = 9$

E. 40; 4; $10 \times 4 = 40$
and $40 \div 4 = 10$

F. 45; 5; $9 \times 5 = 45$
and $45 \div 5 = 9$

S **Add, Subtract, and Multiply**

Solve the following problems using paper and pencil or mental math. Be sure to estimate to see if your answers are reasonable.

1. A. $7980 + 345 =$ B. $60 \times 500 =$

   C. $4021 - 765 =$ D. $3000 - 462 =$

   E. $42 \times 9 =$ F. $38 \times 5 =$

2. Explain your strategy for Question 1D.

TIMS Bit

1. A. 8325   B. 30,000

   C. 3256   D. 2538

   E. 378   F. 190

2. Strategies will vary. Students can use a counting up strategy to subtract.

$462 + 8 = 470$;

$470 + 30 = 500$;

$500 + 2500 = 3000$;

$8 + 30 + 2500 = 2538.$

All Aboard!

Answer the questions below using the following train schedule.

1. 1:37 P.M.

2. 2:30 P.M. train

3. 9:11 A.M.

4. 47 minutes

Leaving Chicago—Going to Roselle					
Chicago	8:30 AM	10:30 AM	12:30 PM	2:30 PM	4:30 PM
Oak Park	8:50 AM	10:50 AM	12:50 PM	2:50 PM	4:50 PM
Itasca	9:03 AM	11:03 AM	1:03 PM	3:03 PM	5:03 PM
Roselle	9:37 AM	11:37 AM	1:37 PM	3:37 PM	5:37 PM

1. Lee Yah and her sister are catching the 12:30 P.M. train in Chicago. At what time will they arrive in Roselle?

2. Irma's mother needs to arrive in Roselle before 4:00 P.M. What is the last train she can take leaving from Chicago?

3. The 8:30 A.M. train from Chicago is delayed 8 minutes. At what time will it arrive in Itasca?

4. Linda and her cousin took the 10:50 A.M. train from Oak Park to Roselle. How long was the train ride?

Student Questions	Teacher Notes

U Quiz: 5s and 10s

A. 30 ÷ 3 =   B. 10 ÷ 1 =

C. 10 ÷ 2 =   D. 60 ÷ 10 =

E. 40 ÷ 8 =   F. 5 ÷ 5 =

G. 20 ÷ 5 =   H. 80 ÷ 10 =

I. 30 ÷ 6 =   J. 35 ÷ 5 =

K. 15 ÷ 3 =   L. 50 ÷ 10 =

M. 70 ÷ 10 =   N. 90 ÷ 9 =

O. 40 ÷ 4 =   P. 20 ÷ 2 =

Q. 100 ÷ 10 =   R. 25 ÷ 5 =

S. 45 ÷ 5 =

TIMS Bit

We recommend 2 minutes for this quiz. Allow students to change pens after the time is up and complete the remaining problems in a different color. After students take the test, have them update their *Division Facts I Know* charts.

It is likely that a student who answers 40 ÷ 8 correctly also knows the answer to 40 ÷ 5. To make sure, after the quiz, ask students to write a related division fact, if possible. The square numbers only have one division sentence (e.g., 25 ÷ 5 = 5). Then, students who answer a fact correctly and who also write the correct related fact, can circle both facts on the chart.

V Who Am I?

Answer each riddle below.

1. I am three less than five squared.

2. I am two times as great as the sum of five and eight.

3. I am half the difference of ten and four.

4. I am six more than the product of nine and three.

5. If you subtract the product of four and three from the sum of eleven and four, you will know who I am.

6. Make up your own riddle to share.

TIMS Challenge

1. 25 − 3 = 22

2. 13 × 2 = 26

3. 6 ÷ 2 = 3

4. 27 + 6 = 33

5. 15 − 12 = 3

6. Answers will vary.

Daily Practice and Problems:
Bit for Lesson 1

A. Angles (URG p. 13)

Use 90° and 180° as benchmarks to draw the following angles.

1. Sketch an angle that is about 95°.
   Tell if your angle is acute, right, or obtuse.

2. Sketch an angle that is about 45°.
   Tell if your angle is acute, right, or obtuse.

3. Sketch an angle that is about 120°.
   Tell if your angle is acute, right, or obtuse.

DPP Task is on page 32. Suggestions for using the DPPs are on page 32.

LESSON GUIDE

Lines

Estimated Class Sessions: 1–2

Students are introduced to geometric vocabulary about lines and line segments. They use the terminology to talk about and solve problems about geometric shapes.

Key Content

- Identifying lines, line segments, rays, and points.
- Identifying parallel and perpendicular lines.
- Describing two-dimensional shapes using their properties.

Key Vocabulary

equilateral triangle	parallelogram
intersect	perpendicular
line	point
line segment	quadrilateral
parallel	ray
parallel lines	

Materials List

Print Materials for Students

		Math Facts and Daily Practice and Problems	Activity	Homework
Student Books	**Student Guide**		*Lines* Pages 238–241	*Lines* Homework Section Page 242
	Discovery Assignment Book			Home Practice Part 1 Page 123
Teacher Resources	**Facts Resource Guide**	DPP Item 9B Use *Triangle Flash Cards: 5s* and *Triangle Flash Cards: 10s* to review the division facts for the 5s and 10s.		
	Unit Resource Guide	DPP Items A–B Pages 13–14		

available on Teacher Resource CD

All Transparency Masters, Blackline Masters, and Assessment Blackline Masters in the Unit Resource Guide are on the Teacher Resource CD.

Supplies for Each Student

ruler

Lines

TIMSville

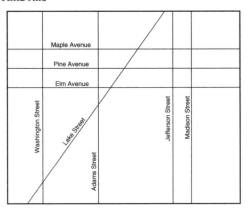

The map of TIMSville shows that Maple Avenue and Pine Avenue go in the same direction. We say Maple Avenue and Pine Avenue are **parallel**. These streets always stay the same distance apart. They will never **intersect** (meet) even if they went on, in the same direction, forever.

Lake Street and Madison Street are not parallel. If you continued them still going straight, they would intersect.

Pine Avenue and Jefferson Street are **perpendicular**. This means they form right angles where they intersect.

Student Guide - Page 238

Washington Street and Lake Street intersect. However, they are not perpendicular.

1. Name a street parallel to Elm Avenue.
2. Name a street parallel to Madison Street.
3. Name a street perpendicular to Maple Avenue.
4. Name a street perpendicular to Washington Street.
5. Name two streets that Lake Street intersects.

On our map of TIMSville, we have drawn straight lines for each street. In mathematics we often just say "**line**" instead of "straight line." For the rest of this unit we will always mean straight line when we say line.

Streets always have a beginning and an end. In mathematics, a line goes on forever in both directions. It has no beginning or end. What we have drawn on our maps are called line segments. A **line segment** has two endpoints. To draw a picture of a line, we draw a line segment and put arrows at the ends to show that it keeps going on infinitely (forever).

Lines are often named by two points on the line. This is line AC.

We write $\overleftrightarrow{AC}$. We can also call it $\overleftrightarrow{AB}$ or $\overleftrightarrow{BC}$.

The line segment AB is the part of the line that starts at A and ends at B. We write $\overline{AB}$ to show that we mean this segment.

6. Name two other line segments that are part of $\overleftrightarrow{AC}$.
7. This is line RT. ($\overleftrightarrow{RT}$)

   A. What are two other names for this line?
   B. Name at least 2 line segments that are part of $\overleftrightarrow{RT}$.

Student Guide - Page 239

Developing the Activity

Throughout this unit, we introduce standard geometric terms so that you and your students will have a common vocabulary for discussing geometric shapes and ideas. The big ideas in this unit, however, are about geometric concepts, not vocabulary. Do not expect that students will become conversant with the geometric terms immediately after they are introduced—and do not delay your instruction of the lessons until students know the vocabulary. Students will more likely learn the proper terms only as they use them over and over again to investigate geometric concepts.

The purpose of this lesson is to introduce some geometric terminology in various contexts. Your students may be familiar with some of these words from their previous work in mathematics or in their daily lives. Sometimes they have used other words to denote the same concept.

Parallel and Perpendicular. Use the map on the *Lines* Activity Pages in the *Student Guide* to discuss parallel streets such as Maple and Pine, and perpendicular streets such as Washington and Elm. Make sure students understand that **parallel** streets always stay the same distance apart and never intersect while streets that are **perpendicular** to one another intersect at right angles. Check that students realize there are several answers to each of the problems in *Questions 1–5.*

Discuss with students that the lines in the maps are really parts of lines (line segments). A line (also called a straight line) is something that goes on infinitely. Unlike streets or line segments, lines never end. Of course, you cannot *really* draw a line, since you would have to keep drawing forever. A **line** is an idea, something we imagine. To represent a line, we draw part of the line and put arrows at each end to mean that it keeps going in both directions, as shown in Figure 7.

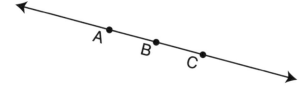

Figure 7: *A line*

We often name lines by naming two points on the line. We mark points with a dot. Points are usually given capital letters as names. Explain to students that the line in Figure 7 can be called line AB or line BA or line AC or line CB, etc. The shorthand for writing line AB is $\overleftrightarrow{AB}$.

Line segments are parts of lines that can be drawn and measured. Line segments have two endpoints. For example, in Figure 7, we see line segment AB (or BA), line segment BC, and line segment CA. The shorthand for writing line segment AB is $\overline{AB}$. This is described in the *Student Guide*.

After discussing the concept of line segments, students answer *Questions 6–7* in the *Student Guide*.

Students are introduced to rays in *Questions 8–9.* A **ray** is similar to a line, but goes on forever in only one direction, as shown in Figure 8. A ray has one endpoint. The shorthand way for writing ray XY is $\overrightarrow{XY}$. A ray is named by saying the endpoint first and then another point on the ray. This ray is called $\overrightarrow{XZ}$ or $\overrightarrow{XY}$, but not $\overrightarrow{ZX}$.

Figure 8: *Ray XY*

Rays are similar to lines, but they go on forever in only one direction. A ray has one endpoint.

8. This is ray XY. We can write ray XY like this: $\overrightarrow{XY}$. A ray is named by its endpoint first, followed by another point on the ray. What is another name for this ray?

9. Name the two rays you see here that make up ∠R.

Talking about Shapes

ABCD is a rectangle. A rectangle has 4 line segments. Each line segment is part of a line. $\overline{AB}$ is part of $\overleftrightarrow{AB}$.

10. A. Name the 4 line segments that make up rectangle ABCD.
    B. $\overline{AD}$ is part of what line?
    C. $\overline{DC}$ is part of what line?
    D. There appear to be two pairs of parallel line segments. Name them.
    E. The angles of a rectangle are right angles. Name a line segment that is perpendicular to $\overline{AB}$.
    F. Name a line segment that is perpendicular to $\overline{CD}$.
    G. Name all the pairs of parallel lines.
    H. Name a line perpendicular to $\overleftrightarrow{AB}$.

Student Guide - Page 240

Content Note

Lines. Children are sometimes confused about the mathematical idea of a line and the everyday word. In math class, we assume a line goes on forever and we try to distinguish between a line and a line segment. However, we would not talk about the 50-yard line segment on a football field!

Parallel Lines. In this lesson, we are looking at lines and other geometric objects drawn on a flat surface. We often say they are "lines in the plane." There are a number of different ways to describe parallel lines in the plane. First, we can say that two lines are parallel if they go in the same direction. Another way to say it is that parallel lines, just like parallel streets, stay the same distance apart. Finally, two lines are parallel if and only if they never meet. Note that you can have two line segments that do not meet, but that are not parallel. For example, in the figure on page 238 in the *Student Guide,* Lake Street and Madison Street represent line segments that do not meet and are not parallel.

Student Guide - Page 241

Question 9 introduced the idea that angles are made of two rays. This will be discussed in Lesson 2. Here, students need to recognize the two rays $\overrightarrow{RS}$ and $\overrightarrow{RT}$.

Talking about Shapes. Explain to students that a shape is usually named by listing its vertices in clockwise or counterclockwise order. This rectangle could be named ABCD or CBAD. You would not say ACBD.

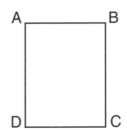

Figure 9: *Rectangle ABCD*

Note to students that each segment is part of a line. Illustrate as in Figure 10 that each segment can be extended to show the line that contains that segment.

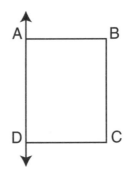

Figure 10: *Rectangle with a side extended into a line*

Ask students to look at the figure in *Question 11,* shown here as Figure 11. You may wish to sketch it on the board or overhead. The figure shown here is a special quadrilateral called a **parallelogram.** Remind students that **quadrilaterals** are shapes that have four sides and four angles. The sides that form this figure are parallel. This means the line segments are parallel as well as the lines. Make sure students realize $\overline{HI}$ is parallel to $\overline{KJ}$ and $\overleftrightarrow{HI}$ is parallel to $\overleftrightarrow{KJ}$. Discuss the other two sides. Students should find that the measures of the opposite sides of the parallelogram are equal.

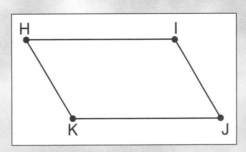

Figure 11: *A parallelogram*

Question 12 asks students whether a rectangle, LMNO, is a parallelogram. Some students may suggest that the figure is not a parallelogram, since it is a rectangle. This misconception is similar to the mistaken belief that a square is not a rectangle. In explaining their reasoning, students need to think about the definition of parallelogram and how it applies, or does not apply, to quadrilateral LMNO. That is, quadrilateral LMNO is a parallelogram because it has two pairs of opposite sides that are parallel. LM is parallel to ON and LO is parallel to MN.

Question 13 asks students to identify all the equilateral triangles they see in the figure shown in Figure 12. Remind students that equilateral triangles have sides of equal length. There are five equilateral triangles in the figure: ABC, BDE, FCE, BEC, and ADF. For *Question 13B,* BC is parallel to DE, EF, and DF. Similarly, CE is parallel to AB, BD, and AD, and BE is parallel to AC, CF, and AF.

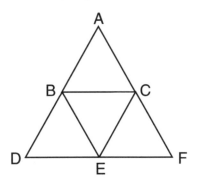

Figure 12: *Equilateral triangles*

Content Note

Parallel. A student may suggest that $\overline{DE}$ is parallel to $\overline{EF}$ in Figure 12. This is correct since a line segment (or line) is parallel to itself.

Daily Practice and Problems: Task for Lesson 1

B. Task: Fact Families for × and ÷
(URG p. 14)

The following four facts are in the same fact family:

$7 \times 10 = 70$ $10 \times 7 = 70$

$70 \div 7 = 10$ $70 \div 10 = 7$

Solve each pair of related number sentences.

Then, give two other facts that are in the same fact family.

A. $5 \times 4 = ?$ and $20 \div 4 = ?$

B. $3 \times 10 = ?$ and $30 \div 3 = ?$

C. $10 \times 5 = ?$ and $50 \div 10 = ?$

D. $8 \times 5 = ?$ and $40 \div 5 = ?$

E. $6 \times 10 = ?$ and $60 \div 6 = ?$

F. $10 \times 8 = ?$ and $80 \div 8 = ?$

Homework

1. Name the line segments that form the sides of the parallelogram.

2. Name three points on the line segment NO.

3. Name the parallel line segments.

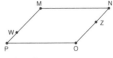

The figure below shows many lines, line segments, and rays.

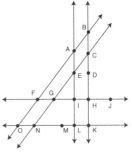

4. One triangle in this figure is triangle GEI. Name at least three other triangles in the figure.

5. Name three pairs of lines that appear to be parallel.

6. Name a pair of lines that appear to be perpendicular.

7. Name three shapes that appear to be parallelograms.

8. Which of the following pairs intersect (meet)?

    A. $\overline{LN}$ and $\overrightarrow{EC}$ B. $\overrightarrow{AF}$ and $\overrightarrow{HI}$

    C. $\overline{IH}$ and $\overline{EC}$ D. $\overleftrightarrow{LK}$ and $\overrightarrow{AB}$

242 SG · Grade 4 · Unit 9 · Lesson 1   Lines

Student Guide - Page 242

Suggestions for Teaching the Lesson

Math Facts

DPP Task B practices multiplication and division within fact families.

Homework and Practice

*   Assign the Homework section in the *Student Guide*. Note: We use the words "appear to be" when asking students to identify perpendicular lines, parallel lines, and various shapes because they are making a judgment based on visual observation. Without actually measuring angles or without extending lines forever, the students do not have enough information to be sure that lines are parallel or perpendicular.

*   DPP item A uses benchmarks to review and draw acute, obtuse, and right angles.

*   Home Practice Part 1 reminds students to use the *Triangle Flash Cards* to study the division facts for the fives and tens. *Triangle Flash Cards: 5s* and *Triangle Flash Cards: 10s* were distributed in Unit 8 Lesson 8 in the *Discovery Assignment Book*.

Extension

Have students look for examples of lines in their environment that appear to be parallel or perpendicular. Examples of perpendicular lines might include the lines forming the corner of square tiles on the floor or the lines forming the corners of a rectangular piece of paper. Examples of parallel lines might include the parallel lines painted in a parking lot or the parallel lines formed on opposite sides of a windowpane.

Name _____ Date _____

Unit 9: Home Practice

Part 1 *Triangle Flash Cards: 5s and 10s*

Study for the quiz on the multiplication facts for the 5s and 10s. Take home your *Triangle Flash Cards* and your list of facts you need to study.

Here's how to use the flash cards. Ask a family member to choose one flash card at a time. Your partner should cover one of the smaller numbers. (One of the smaller numbers is in a circle. The other number is in a square.) Solve a division fact using the two uncovered numbers. Go through the cards a second time, this time cover the other small number.

Your teacher will tell you when the quiz on the 5s and 10s will be. Remember to concentrate on one small group of facts each night—about 8 to 10 facts. Also, remember to concentrate on those facts you cannot answer correctly and quickly.

Part 2 **Mental Multiplication**

1. Use mental math to solve Questions 1A–1F.

   A. $6000 \times 10 =$ _____ **B.** $500 \times 70 =$ _____

   C. $60 \times 60 =$ _____ **D.** $9000 \times 5 =$ _____

   E. $100 \times 800 =$ _____ **F.** $500 \times 50 =$ _____

2. **A.** Paper towels cost 80¢. How much will 6 rolls cost?

   B. One ice cream bar costs $3.50. How much will 4 bars cost?

   C. Bagels cost 69¢ each. About how much will 5 bagels cost?

3. How much is:
   A. 13 nickels?

   B. 11 nickels and 5 dimes?

   C. 5 quarters and 17 nickels?

SHAPES AND SOLIDS   DAB · Grade 4 · Unit 9 123

Discovery Assignment Book - Page 123

AT A GLANCE

Math Facts and Daily Practice and Problems

For DPP item A students use benchmarks to identify and draw angles. Task B uses fact families to practice multiplication and division facts.

Developing the Activity

1. Discuss parallel and perpendicular lines using *Questions 1–5* on the *Lines* Activity Pages in the *Student Guide.*
2. Students discuss lines, line segments, and rays using *Questions 6–9.*
3. Discuss the Talking about Shapes section in the *Student Guide* and complete *Questions 10–13.*

Homework

1. Students complete the homework questions in the *Student Guide.*
2. Assign Home Practice Part 1 which reminds students to use the *Triangle Flash Cards* to study the math facts for the fives and tens.

Notes:

Student Guide

Questions 1–13 (SG pp. 239–241)

1. Pine Ave. or Maple Ave.

2. Jefferson St., Adams St., or Washington St.

3. Washington St., Adams St., Jefferson St., or Madison St.

4. Maple Ave., Pine Ave., or Elm Ave.

5. Students name two of the following: Washington St., Adams St., Elm Ave., Pine Ave., or Maple Ave. If Lake Street and Jefferson and Madison continue, Lake will intersect both.

6. $\overline{BC}$ and $\overline{AC}$

7. **A.** $\overleftrightarrow{RS}$ and $\overleftrightarrow{ST}$

   B. Students give two of the following: $\overline{RS}$, $\overline{ST}$, $\overline{RT}$

8. $\overline{XZ}$

9. $\overrightarrow{RS}$ and $\overrightarrow{RT}$

10. **A.** $\overline{AB}$, $\overline{BC}$, $\overline{CD}$, and $\overline{DA}$

    B. $\overleftrightarrow{AD}$

    C. $\overleftrightarrow{DC}$

    D. $\overline{AB}$ & $\overline{CD}$, $\overline{DA}$ & $\overline{BC}$

    E. $\overline{DA}$ or $\overline{BC}$

    F. $\overline{DA}$ or $\overline{BC}$

    G. $\overleftrightarrow{AB}$, $\overleftrightarrow{DC}$, and $\overleftrightarrow{AD}$, $\overleftrightarrow{BC}$

    H. $\overleftrightarrow{AD}$, $\overleftrightarrow{BC}$

11. **A.** *$\overline{HI}$ is parallel to $\overline{JK}$, $\overline{HK}$ is parallel to $\overline{IJ}$

    B. *$\overleftrightarrow{HI}$ is parallel to $\overleftrightarrow{KJ}$, $\overleftrightarrow{HK}$ is parallel to $\overleftrightarrow{IJ}$

    C. *The line segments which are parallel to one another have the same length.

12. *Yes. Quadrilateral LMNO is a parallelogram: it has two pairs of opposite sides that are parallel.

13. **A.** *ABC, DBE, BCE, CFE, ADF

    B. *$\overline{BC}$ is parallel to $\overline{DE}$, $\overline{EF}$, and $\overline{DF}$; $\overline{CE}$ is parallel to $\overline{AB}$, $\overline{BD}$, and $\overline{DA}$, $\overline{BE}$ is parallel to $\overline{AF}$, $\overline{AC}$, and $\overline{CF}$.

Homework (SG p. 242)

Questions 1–8

1. $\overline{MN}$, $\overline{ON}$, $\overline{OP}$, $\overline{PM}$

2. Points N, Z, and O

3. $\overline{MN}$ is parallel to $\overline{OP}$; $\overline{MW}$, $\overline{WP}$ and $\overline{MP}$ are parallel to $\overline{NZ}$, $\overline{ZO}$ and $\overline{NO}$.

4. Students name at least three triangles. Answers will vary. Possible answers include: OAL, FAI, NEL, OBK, NCK, GCH, FBH

5. $\overleftrightarrow{OB}$ & $\overleftrightarrow{NC}$, $\overleftrightarrow{FJ}$ & $\overleftrightarrow{OK}$, $\overleftrightarrow{LA}$ & $\overleftrightarrow{BK}$
   [Note: Names for the lines may vary.]

6. Answers will vary. Possible answers include: $\overleftrightarrow{LA}$ & $\overleftrightarrow{OK}$, $\overleftrightarrow{BK}$ & $\overleftrightarrow{OK}$, $\overleftrightarrow{LA}$ & $\overleftrightarrow{FJ}$, $\overleftrightarrow{BK}$ & $\overleftrightarrow{FJ}$

   [Note: Names for the lines may vary.]

7. Answers will vary. FGNO, IHKL, BCEA

8. B and D

*Answers and/or discussion are included in the Lesson Guide.

**Answers for all the Home Practice in the *Discovery Assignment Book* are at the end of the unit.

LESSON GUIDE

What's Your Angle?

Estimated Class Sessions: 2

The concepts of angle and angle measure are reviewed. Students learn to measure angles using a protractor.

Key Content

*   Naming angles.
*   Identifying acute, obtuse, and right angles.
*   Measuring angles with a protractor.

Key Vocabulary

acute angle
degrees
endpoint
obtuse angle
point
polygon
protractor
quadrilateral
ray
right angle
vertex

Daily Practice and Problems: Bits for Lesson 2

C. Practicing the Facts (URG p. 14)

A. $5 \div 1 =$ B. $40 \div 4 =$

C. $15 \div 3 =$ D. $100 \div 10 =$

E. $45 \div 5 =$ F. $25 \div 5 =$

G. $60 \div 10 =$ H. $35 \div 7 =$

I. $10 \div 5 =$ J. $30 \div 5 =$

K. $0 \div 5 =$

E. Division Stories (URG p. 15)

The following two problems can be solved using division.

1. Mrs. Randall gave each of her children $4 to spend on games at the neighborhood carnival. If Mrs. Randall gave out $20 in all, how many children does she have? Draw a picture to show this problem.

2. One package of bus tokens contains 10 tokens. Keenya's mother needs 40 tokens to get to and from work for one month. How many packages does Keenya's mother need? Draw a picture to show this problem.

DPP Tasks are on page 44. Suggestions for using the DPPs are on page 44.

Curriculum Sequence

Before This Unit

Students were introduced to angles and degree measures in Unit 2.

Materials List

Print Materials for Students

	Math Facts and Daily Practice and Problems	Activity	Homework	Written Assessment
Student Books — Student Guide		*What's Your Angle?* Pages 243–248	*What's Your Angle?* Homework Section Pages 248–250	
Student Books — Discovery Assignment Book		*Measuring Angles I* Page 127	Home Practice Part 2 Page 123	*Measuring Angles II* Page 129
Teacher Resources — Facts Resource Guide	DPP Items 9C & 9E			
Teacher Resources — Unit Resource Guide	DPP Items C–F Pages 14–16			

available on Teacher Resource CD

All Transparency Masters, Blackline Masters, and Assessment Blackline Masters in the Unit Resource Guide are on the Teacher Resource CD.

Supplies for Each Student

protractor
cardboard corner or plastic right triangle, optional

Materials for the Teacher

Transparency of *Measuring Angles I* Activity Page (Discovery Assignment Book) Page 127, optional
Transparency of *Measuring Angles II* Activity Page (Discovery Assignment Book) Page 129, optional
Observational Assessment Record (Unit Resource Guide, Pages 9–10 and Teacher Resource CD)
cardboard corner or plastic right triangle
protractor

Before the Activity

Be sure to discuss DPP item A, which reviews acute, obtuse, and right angles.

Developing the Activity

Part 1. Looking at Angles

Begin the class by asking your students to turn to the *What's Your Angle?* Activity Pages in the *Student Guide.* The opening picture and text compare airplanes taking off. See Figure 13. Discuss **Question 1.** When an airplane leaves the ground, its course is determined by the angle of climbing, that is, the angle that it makes with the ground. If both airplanes fly at the same speed, which plane will be higher in the air after several seconds? Ask students to explain how they know.

Eventually focus their attention on the opening of the angle. The lengths of the sides of the angles in the picture are about equal. Ask:

- *What if the lengths of the sides of one of the angles were changed? Would this change your prediction of which plane climbs higher faster?*

Make a sketch on the blackboard or overhead of these two angles. Extend the sides of one of the angles and discuss whether this makes the angle bigger. The purpose here is to reinforce the ideas that were explored in Unit 2: that the amount of opening of the angle is the important characteristic, not the length of the sides.

Figure 13: *Two angles of climbing*

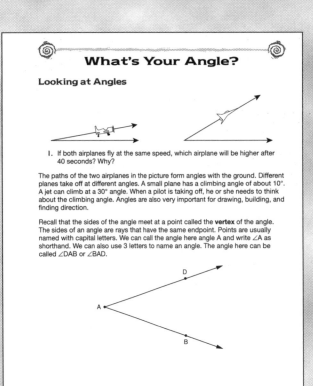

1. If both airplanes fly at the same speed, which airplane will be higher after 40 seconds? Why?

The paths of the two airplanes in the picture form angles with the ground. Different planes take off at different angles. A small plane has a climbing angle of about 10°. A jet can climb at a 30° angle. When a pilot is taking off, he or she needs to think about the climbing angle. Angles are also very important for drawing, building, and finding direction.

Recall that the sides of the angle meet at a point called the **vertex** of the angle. The sides of an angle are rays that have the same endpoint. Points are usually named with capital letters. We can call the angle here angle A and write ∠A as shorthand. We can also use 3 letters to name an angle. The angle here can be called ∠DAB or ∠BAD.

Student Guide - Page 243

Content Note

Angle of Climbing. Figure 13 is a simplified picture of an airplane's takeoff. The true path looks more like the figure below, i.e., when the plane is just lifting off, the climb angle is small and eventually becomes constant.

The sides of an angle are two **rays** with the same endpoint. The endpoint is called the **vertex** of the angle. Explain to students that the vertex of an angle is a **point** and is often named with a letter. The convention is to refer to an angle by the name of the vertex, if it causes no confusion. Otherwise, three letters are used to name an angle. For example, we can refer to $\angle A$ or $\angle DAB$ or $\angle BAD$ in Figure 14, where B and D are points on the sides of the angle. If the measure of $\angle A$ is $37°$, we use a shorthand notation and write $\angle A = 37°$.

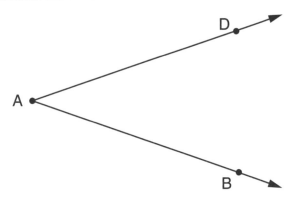

Figure 14: *Naming an angle*

Review the notion of angles as turning, discussed in Unit 2, by asking questions such as:

- *How many degrees do you make when you turn a complete circle?* (360°)

- *How many degrees do you make when you turn a half circle?* (180°)

- *How many degrees do you make when you turn a quarter circle?* (90°)

Illustrate making angles by holding two pencils together (or a pair of scissors). Slowly move one of the pencils to show the formation of an angle as illustrated in Figure 15. Make several angles like this and have students estimate about how many degrees you turned. Suggest students use 90° and 180° as benchmarks, as they did in Unit 2. The pencils represent the sides (or rays) of the angle. The number of degrees is a way of describing or measuring the amount of turning of an angle, that is, the amount of opening of an angle. Students should realize that the greater the degree measure, the larger the opening. Emphasize again that using longer pencils does not make the angles bigger.

Figure 15: *Forming an angle*

Ask students to identify angles that already exist in the classroom. For example, draw students' attention to the top surface of their books. The edges form a 90° angle. Discuss the sides and vertices of angles. The hands of the clock form angles. Ask students to look around the room and find more examples of angles. Students may note corners of tables, papers, or boxes. Ask students to find angles that do not appear to be 90°.

Remind students that an angle that measures 90° is called a **right angle.** Angles that measure less than 90° are **acute angles;** angles that measure more than 90° are **obtuse angles.**

Draw some angles on the blackboard or overhead and ask students to estimate their measures, using benchmarks. Ask:

- *Is the angle greater than 90°? Less than 90°?*
- *Is the angle about halfway between 90° and 180°?*
- *What angle is halfway between 0° and 90°?*
- *What angle is halfway between 90° and 180°?*

We frequently need to draw or measure 90° angles. To do this, a cardboard corner or a plastic right triangle or square can be used. Use a straightedge to draw angles on the overhead or blackboard that are close to 90°.

TIMS Tip
Make sure you vary the orientation of the angles you draw on the overhead projector or blackboard. Include angles that do not have a side sitting on the horizontal and that open in different directions.

Content Note
We simplify this discussion by only considering angles that are at most 180 degrees. Of course, angles can be greater than 180 degrees. For example, in the diagram below we can measure the smaller angle or the larger angle.

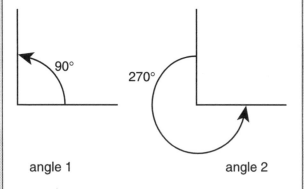

angle 1   angle 2

If we think of angles as indicating the amount of turning, then angles have a direction (clockwise or counterclockwise) as well as a magnitude. But we leave that discussion for later grades.

Ask students to estimate whether the various angles are 90° or not. Ask students to come to the board or overhead and determine whether the angle you drew on the board was indeed less than 90, greater than 90, or 90 degrees using a cardboard corner or some other right angle. Draw some of the angles opening to the left, or opening down. Draw some angles with short sides and some with unequal sides as shown in Figure 16. This helps children realize that it is the amount of opening that is important, not the sides.

Figure 16: *Various angles*

Part 2. Measuring Angles

In order to measure angles other than 90°, we use a protractor. Remind students that we are measuring the amount of opening or turning between the two sides of the angle. Point out to the students that there are two sets of numbers from 0 to 180 on the protractor, one appearing clockwise, the other counterclockwise. Remind students that 180° is half a circle, while 360° is a full circle. Explain that one of the sides (or rays) of the angle to be measured must always be on the bottom line (the 0 degree line) and the vertex of the angle must be in the center of this line segment. Some protractors have a hole at the center.

Make sure that students understand to use the set of numbers that begins where one of the sides of the angle lies. For example, since a side of the angle in Figure 17 lies on the left side of the hole, we use the outer set of numbers since they begin on the left side and read the angle measure as 46°. A side of the angle in *Question 2* in the *Student Guide* lies on the right, so we use the inner set of numbers. Remind students to look at the angle first and determine whether the angle is greater than or less than 90°. This will reduce the number of errors.

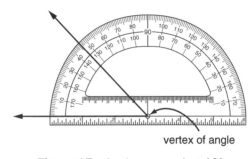

vertex of angle

Figure 17: *Angle measuring 46°*

Measuring Angles

We measure the opening between the two sides of the angle in degrees. Protractors are used to measure angles. The measure of the angle shown here lies between 70° and 80°. Angle Z measures 73°. We write ∠Z = 73°. Notice where the vertex of the angle is placed.

2. Is the angle shown above an acute or an obtuse angle?

3. A. Is the measure of this angle less than or greater than 90°?

B. Between which two numbers on the protractor does the measure of this angle lie?

C. What is the measure of the angle?

244 SG · Grade 4 · Unit 9 · Lesson 2   What's Your Angle?

Student Guide - Page 244

In *Questions 3–4* in the *Student Guide,* students are asked to name the numbers on the protractor between which the measure of the given angle lies. Focus students' attention on these two numbers. *Question 3A* asks if the angle shown is greater than or less than 90 degrees. When students have determined that the angle is less than 90 degrees, they can easily choose the correct scale to use on the protractor and see that the angle has a measure between 50 and 60 degrees. *(Question 3B)* To the nearest degree, the angle measures 57 degrees. *(Question 3C)* To answer *Question 4,* they must first determine that the angle is greater than 90 degrees, so that they know which scale to read on the protractor. The angle lies between 120° and 130°. It helps children read the scale correctly when they look at the numbers and recognize the direction of the numbers on the scale.

Ask students to measure the angles on the *Measuring Angles I* Activity Page in the *Discovery Assignment Book.* The angles on this page were made large enough so that the sides need not be extended when measuring with most protractors.

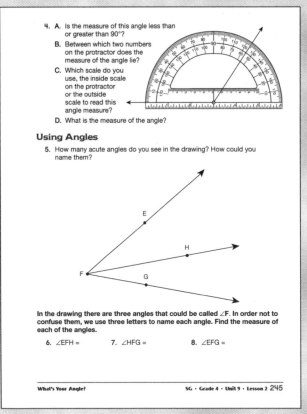

Student Guide - Page 245

🅣IMS Tip

Some protractors begin the numbering scale at the very bottom edge of the protractor. That is, the 0° line is the bottom edge of the protractor. If any of your students have such protractors, make sure they are able to use them correctly.

Content Note

It is important for children to understand the limits of accuracy in measuring. While we measure an angle and say it is 90°, the accuracy is at best to the nearest degree. Note that the measurement tools we have available are not very precise. Engineers, architects, and other professionals have tools that are much more accurate, but no tool is perfect. In work with angle measures, accept measures that are off by a degree or two because of the imprecision of measurement tools, line thickness, and other factors.

Draw an angle on the overhead or blackboard whose sides are not long enough to reach the scale on the protractor. Ask what you should do in order to measure this angle accurately. Students should suggest extending the sides of an angle in order to measure accurately. Explain to students that this often happens when measuring figures containing several angles. Remind them that the lengths of the sides of the angle do not determine the angle. The sides of an angle are rays. Rays go on forever in one direction so they can extend the sides as long as they like. Remind them to use a straightedge (the straight side of the protractor or a ruler) to extend the sides. It is not acceptable to

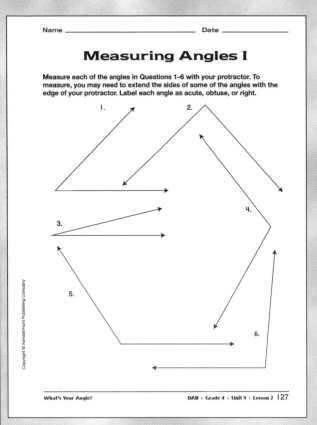

Discovery Assignment Book - Page 127

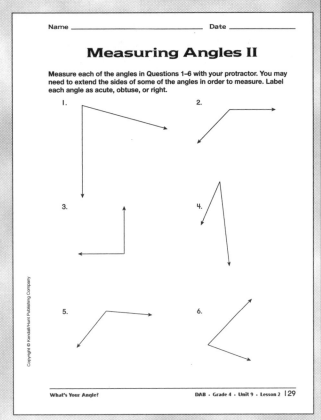

Discovery Assignment Book - Page 129

The park district for the town of TIMSville has decided to build a new playground. One of the features will be a sandbox for little children. The town is asking for designs for the sandbox. A design for the sandbox must have all straight sides. The sandbox will be located between two sidewalks that meet at a 50° angle. So, one of the angles of the sandbox must be 50°.

Here is the design Ana submitted. She used the scale 1 cm = 1 foot.

9. Design a sandbox for TIMSville's new playground. Your sandbox can have a different number of sides.

10. Design a different sandbox for the playground.

What's Your Angle?

Student Guide - Page 246

---

extend the sides free-hand (unless you are estimating). Measure several more angles on the overhead together, asking students to come up and do the measuring.

Use the *Measuring Angles II* Activity Page in the *Discovery Assignment Book* as an assessment of students' abilities to measure angles. For some of these angles, the students will have to extend the sides in order to measure accurately.

Part 3. Using Angles

After students have practiced measuring angles, use *Questions 5–12* in the Using Angles section in the *Student Guide* to explore angles in different settings. Encourage students to extend the sides of the angles with the straight edge on their protractor to improve the accuracy of their measurements. *Questions 5–8* ask students to measure three overlapping angles. Make sure students see that the sum of measures of the smaller two angles is the measure of the larger angle. Note that in this case, naming the angles by their vertex (F) is not clear. The angles need to be named by three letters, such as EFH.

Questions 9–10 challenge students to construct their own angles. You can give students additional practice constructing angles by challenging them to draw angles of specific measure at their seats while you model the process at the overhead. *Question 9* requires students to construct a sandbox (a polygon) that contains a 50° angle. The sandbox can have any number of sides. Give students a chance to try to construct an angle of 50° and discuss their methods as a group. Make sure that the angles they draw are fairly accurate. If no one suggests an accurate method, explain that they can draw an angle by first drawing one of the sides (rays) with a straightedge and picking a point for the vertex. Then, they should place the protractor so that the vertex is on the hole in the protractor and the drawn side of the angle matches the 0° line. Mark with a point the desired degrees as shown in Figure 18. Then, use the straightedge to draw the line between the dot and the vertex.

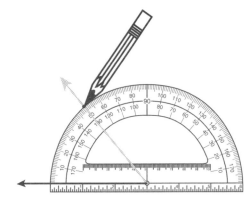

Figure 18: *Drawing an angle*

Discuss polygons within the context of designing sandboxes. Begin by drawing a polygon on the board or overhead. An example is shown in Figure 19. Explain that a **polygon** is a many-sided (or angled) figure. Point out to students that a polygon is made up of line segments that are all connected. The sides never overlap and the polygon is closed. That is, each endpoint of every side meets with the endpoint of another side. Discuss the examples of polygons and nonpolygons in the *Student Guide*. The first shape (shape W) in *Question 11* is not a polygon because it overlaps; the second shape is not a polygon because it is not closed, the third shape is not made up of line segments, and the fourth shape is not connected (because it is two parts).

A four-sided polygon is called a **quadrilateral.** Draw a quadrilateral on the board or overhead. Name and measure all the angles of the quadrilateral you have drawn. Show students how to place the protractor in order to measure all the angles. Remind them that they can turn their books or papers to make measuring easier. They may need to extend the sides of a polygon in order to measure as well. Remind students that a polygon is usually named by listing its vertices in clockwise or counterclockwise order. This polygon could be named ABCD or CBAD. You would not say ACBD.

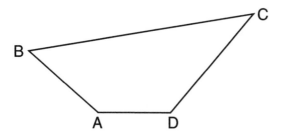

Figure 19: *Quadrilateral ABCD*

Students may need to use a ruler to trace the polygon in *Question 12* on a separate sheet of paper before measuring.

 Journal Prompt
Explain why the measure of an angle does not depend on the length of the sides of the angle.

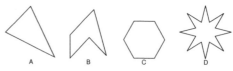
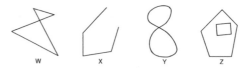

Shapes like the one Ana designed for the playground are called polygons. A **polygon** is a figure whose sides are line segments that are all connected. Every endpoint of a side meets the endpoint of exactly one other side and no sides overlap. The word *polygon* comes from the prefix *poly* (many) and suffix *gon* (angles). So, a polygon has many angles (or you could say many sides).

These shapes are polygons:

A   B   C   D

These shapes are not polygons:

W   X   Y   Z

11. Explain why each of the shapes above is not a polygon.

Student Guide - Page 247

Daily Practice and Problems: Tasks for Lesson 2

D. Task: Multiplication Practice
(URG p. 15)

Solve the following problems using paper and pencil. Estimate to make sure your answers are reasonable.

1. A. $48 \times 5 =$ B. $88 \times 8 =$

   C. $65 \times 5 =$ D. $54 \times 4 =$

   E. $27 \times 5 =$ F. $74 \times 7 =$

2. Explain your estimation strategy for Question 1C.

F. Task: Money (URG p. 16)

1. What coins can be used to make 16 cents? How many different ways can you answer this?

2. What is the least number of coins you can use to make 35 cents? Tell which coins.

3. What is the greatest number of coins you can use to make 40 cents? Tell which coins.

Suggestions for Teaching the Lesson

Math Facts

DPP Bit C practices the division facts for the 5s and 10s. Bit E uses division to solve problems.

Homework and Practice

- Assign the Homework section in the *Student Guide.* Students will need a protractor to complete the questions.

- DPP Task D provides multiplication practice. Task F develops number sense working with money.

- Remind students to use the *Triangle Flash Cards: 5s* and *10s* to study for the quiz on the division facts that will be administered in DPP Bit U. The flash cards were distributed in Unit 8 Lesson 8 in the *Discovery Assignment Book.* Flash cards are also available in the Generic Section.

- Assign Home Practice Part 2 to practice mental multiplication and multiplication with money,

Answers for Part 2 of the Home Practice can be found in the Answer Key at the end of this lesson and at the end of this unit.

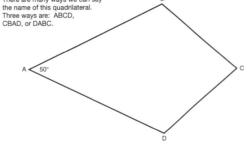

We often name polygons with letters. When we say the name, we go around the shape. For example, the shape Ana drew is a quadrilateral. A **quadrilateral** is a polygon with 4 sides (or we can say 4 angles).

There are many ways we can say the name of this quadrilateral. Three ways are: ABCD, CBAD, or DABC.

12. Find measures of all the angles in Ana's quadrilateral. Use a ruler to trace the design on another sheet of paper first.

   A. ∠A =   B. ∠B =   C. ∠C =   D. ∠D =

Homework

You will need a protractor to complete this homework.

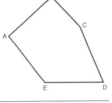

1. Nila made a design for a sandbox. Her design is shown here. She labeled the angles A, B, C, D, and E. The sandbox needed to have a 130° angle.
   A. Which angle do you think is 130°?

Student Guide - Page 248

B. Trace the design on another paper, extend the sides with the edge of your protractor, and measure the angles of Nila's design.
   ∠A =
   ∠B =
   ∠C =
   ∠D =
   ∠E =
   C. List 5 ways to name Nila's design.

2. Design a 3-sided sandbox for a playground. All the sides must be straight and there must be a 45° angle in the design.

3. Design a 6-sided sandbox for a playground. All the sides must be straight and there must be a 90° angle in the design.

4. A. Use a ruler to trace this figure first. Then, find the measure of the angles.
   ∠RST = ?
   ∠TSU = ?
   ∠RSU = ?
   B. What is the sum of the measures of ∠RST and ∠TSU? How does the sum compare to the measure of ∠RSU?

5. James works for the Sparkling Clean Window Washing company. His boss told him that when using a ladder to clean windows, the ladder must make an angle with the ground between 65° and 75° in order to be safe to climb. The picture here shows a ladder leaning against a building.
   A. What is the measure of the angle between the ladder and the ground?
   B. Will this ladder be safe to climb?
   C. What is the measure of the angle between the ladder and the building (the top angle)?
   D. What is the measure of the angle between the house and the ground?

Student Guide - Page 249

Assessment

- Use the *Measuring Angles II* Activity Page in the *Discovery Assignment Book* to assess students' facility with measuring angles and identifying acute, obtuse, and right angles.

- Assess students' abilities to measure and identify types of angles as they work. Record your observations on the *Observational Assessment Record*.

6. The picture below shows many angles. Describe 5 angles you see in the picture.

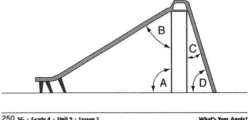

7. Here is a side view of a playground slide. Measure the angles.

∠A =
∠B =
∠C =
∠D =

What's Your Angle?

***Student Guide* - Page 250**

Name _____ Date _____

Unit 9: Home Practice

Part 1 *Triangle Flash Cards: 5s and 10s*

Study for the quiz on the multiplication facts for the 5s and 10s. Take home your *Triangle Flash Cards* and your list of facts you need to study.

Here's how to use the flash cards. Ask a family member to choose one flash card at a time. Your partner should cover one of the smaller numbers. (One of the smaller numbers is in a circle. The other number is in a square.) Solve a division fact using the two uncovered numbers. Go through the cards a second time, this time cover the other small number.

Your teacher will tell you when the quiz on the 5s and 10s will be. Remember to concentrate on one small group of facts each night—about 8 to 10 facts. Also, remember to concentrate on those facts you cannot answer correctly and quickly.

Part 2 **Mental Multiplication**

1. Use mental math to solve Questions 1A–1F.

   A. $6000 \times 10 =$ _____
   B. $500 \times 70 =$ _____
   C. $60 \times 60 =$ _____
   D. $9000 \times 5 =$ _____
   E. $100 \times 800 =$ _____
   F. $500 \times 50 =$ _____

2. **A.** Paper towels cost 80¢. How much will 6 rolls cost?

   B. One ice cream bar costs $3.50. How much will 4 bars cost?

   C. Bagels cost 69¢ each. About how much will 5 bagels cost?

3. How much is:
   A. 13 nickels?

   B. 11 nickels and 5 dimes?

   C. 5 quarters and 17 nickels?

***Discovery Assignment Book* - Page 123**

AT A GLANCE

Math Facts and Daily Practice and Problems

DPP Bits C and E provide division facts practice. Task D practices multiplication. Task F develops number sense by working with money.

Part 1. Looking at Angles

1. Review angles and angle measure using *Question 1* on the *What's Your Angle?* Activity Pages in the *Student Guide.*
2. Discuss that the sides of angles are two rays.
3. Review 360°, 180°, and 90° angles.
4. Review acute, obtuse, and right angles and how to name angles.

Part 2. Measuring Angles

1. Discuss how to measure an angle with a protractor in different directions with sides of differing lengths. Use *Questions 2–4* on the *What's Your Angle?* Activity Pages as a guide.
2. Students complete *Measuring Angles I* Activity Page in the *Discovery Assignment Book.*

Part 3. Using Angles

1. Discuss the measure of angles that overlap using *Questions 5–8.*
2. Discuss drawing angles using a protractor.
3. Students draw shapes with angles of a given measure in *Questions 9–10.*
4. Discuss polygons and measuring the angles of a polygon.

Homework

1. Students complete the Homework section.
2. Remind students to study the division facts for the fives and tens with a family member using *Triangle Flash Cards.*
3. Assign Part 2 of the Home Practice to develop mental math skills.

Assessment

1. Use the *Measuring Angles II* Activity Page in the *Discovery Assignment Book* to assess students' abilities to measure and identify types of angles.
2. Use the *Observational Assessment Record* to record your observations of students as they measure and identify types of angles.

Notes:

Student Guide

Questions 1–12 (SG pp. 243–248)

1. *The airplane on the right will be higher after 40 seconds.

2. acute angle

3. **A.** *less than 90°
   B. *between 50° and 60°
   C. *57°

4. **A.** *greater than 90°
   B. *120° and 130°
   C. outside
   D. 124°

5. *3 acute angles: ∠EFH, ∠HFG, & ∠EFG

6. ∠EFH = 30°

7. ∠HFG = 20°

8. ∠EFG = 50°

9. *Answers will vary.

10. *Answers will vary.

11. *The first shape (W) is not a polygon because it overlaps; the second shape (X) is not a polygon because it is not closed; the third shape (Y) is not made up of line segments; and the fourth shape is not connected (because it is two parts).

12. *Accept angle measures within 1 or 2 degrees:
    A. ∠A = 50°
    B. ∠B = 116°
    C. ∠C = 79°
    D. ∠D = 115°

Homework (SG pp. 248–250)

Questions 1–7

1. **A.** Answers will vary. ∠A and ∠B both look like right angles and ∠D looks to be less than 90°. That leaves only ∠E amd ∠C as possibly 130°.
   B. Accept answers within 1° or 2°: ∠A = 90°, ∠B = 90°, ∠C = 160°, ∠D = 66°, ∠E = 130°
   C. Answers will vary. Five possible answers: ABCDE, BCDEA, CDEAB, EDCBA, AEDCB

2. Answers will vary.

3. Answers will vary.

4. **A.** Accept answers within 1° or 2°: ∠RST = 30°, ∠TSU = 120°, ∠RSU = 150°
   B. 150°, Sum is equal to the measure of ∠RSU.

5. **A.** 73° (Accept measures within 1° or 2°.)
   B. Yes, the angle is between 65° and 75°.
   C. 17°
   D. 90°

6. Answers will vary. Possible answers include: The angle formed by the two legs of the top of the swing set is an acute angle, the horizontal bars on the merry-go-round are right angles, etc.

7. Accept answers within 1° or 2°. ∠A = 90°, ∠B = 60°, ∠C = 18°, ∠D = 73°

*Answers and/or discussion are included in the Lesson Guide.
**Answers for all the Home Practice in the *Discovery Assignment Book* are at the end of the unit.

Discovery Assignment Book

**Home Practice (DAB p. 123)

Part 2. Mental Multiplication

Questions 1–3

1. A. 60,000
    B. 35,000
    C. 3600
    D. 45,000
    E. 80,000
    F. 25,000
2. A. $4.80
    B. $14
    C. about $3.50
3. A. 65¢
    B. $1.05
    C. $2.10

Measuring Angles I (DAB p. 127)

Questions 1–6

Accept measures within 1° or 2°.

1. 45°, acute
2. 90°, right
3. 13°, acute
4. 111°, obuse
5. 125°, obtuse
6. 95°, obtuse

Measuring Angles II (DAB p. 129)

Questions 1–6

Accept measures within 1° or 2°.

1. 75°, acute
2. 135°, obtuse
3. 90°, right
4. 32°, acute
5. 126°, obtuse
6. 64°, acute

*Answers and/or discussion are included in the Lesson Guide.

**Answers for all the Home Practice in the *Discovery Assignment Book* are at the end of the unit.

LESSON GUIDE

Symmetry

Estimated Class Sessions: 2

Turn (rotational) symmetry and line (reflective) symmetry are explored.

Key Content

- Identifying turn (rotational) symmetry.
- Identifying line (reflective) symmetry.

Key Vocabulary

angle of turning
center of turning (rotation)
hexagon
line of symmetry
line (reflective) symmetry
rhombus
trapezoid
triangle
turn (rotational) symmetry
type of turn symmetry

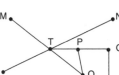
Curriculum Sequence

Before This Unit

Symmetry. Students explored symmetry in pattern blocks and pattern block designs in first and second grade. In Grade 3 Unit 12 Lesson 3, students identified lines of symmetry in shapes.

After This Unit

Symmetry. Spinners will be used in exploring probability in Unit 14, *Chancy Predictions*. Students use their knowledge of angles and turn symmetry to create game spinners.

Materials List

Print Materials for Students

	Math Facts and Daily Practice and Problems	Activity	Homework	Written Assessment
Student Guide		*Symmetry* Pages 251–255		
Discovery Assignment Book		*Pattern Block Shapes* Page 131, *Line Symmetry Examples* Page 133, *Turn Symmetry Examples* Page 135, and *Blank Spinners* Page 137	Home Practice Part 3 Page 124 and *More Symmetry* Page 139	
Unit Resource Guide	DPP Items G–J Pages 16–18 ⊙			DPP Item I *Geometric Gems* Page 17 ⊙

(Rows grouped as **Student Books**: Student Guide, Discovery Assignment Book; **Teacher Resource**: Unit Resource Guide)

⊙ *available on Teacher Resource CD*

All Transparency Masters, Blackline Masters, and Assessment Blackline Masters in the Unit Resource Guide are on the Teacher Resource CD.

Supplies for Each Student

4 blank pages, and extras
pattern blocks, a few of each shape
protractor
ruler
scissors
calculator
envelope, optional

Materials for the Teacher

3 transparencies of *Pattern Block Shapes* Activity Page (Discovery Assignment Book) Page 131
Transparency of *Line Symmetry Examples* Activity Page (Discovery Assignment Book) Page 133, optional
Transparency of *Turn Symmetry Examples* Activity Page (Discovery Assignment Book) Page 135, optional
Transparency of *Blank Spinners* Activity Page (Discovery Assignment Book) Page 137, optional
Observational Assessment Record (Unit Resource Guide, Pages 9–10 and Teacher Resource CD)
large square cut out of construction paper for class demonstration
protractor

Before the Activity

Cut out a large square from light-colored construction paper. A square 8 inches by 8 inches should be large enough for demonstration purposes.

You will need two transparencies of the *Pattern Block Shapes* Activity Page in the *Discovery Assignment Book* for this activity. Leave one transparency intact. Cut out the shapes on the second transparency.

Developing the Activity

Part 1. Line (Reflective) Symmetry

Figures with **line symmetry** have a line (or lines) of symmetry. If the figure is folded on the **line of symmetry,** the two parts match exactly. We can say that the two parts are mirror images of each other.

Use a large square to illustrate one of the lines of symmetry in a square. Fold the square on a line of symmetry. Be sure students see that the two parts match exactly. Unfold the square and draw a line with a marker to show this line of symmetry. Ask students if the square has any other lines of symmetry. Call on volunteers to show the class how to find the other lines by folding the square in half and drawing a line along each fold. Figure 20 shows the four lines of symmetry in a square.

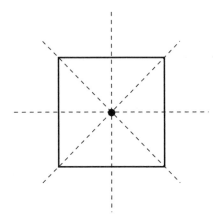

Figure 20: *A square has four lines of symmetry.*

Ask students to turn to the *Pattern Block Shapes* Activity Page in the *Discovery Assignment Book.* Students cut out the shapes and fold them to determine which of the shapes have line symmetry. Remind students to mark each line of symmetry that they find with a pencil or pen, using a ruler as a guide. The right triangle and the small trapezoid do not have line symmetry. The equilateral triangle has 3 lines of symmetry; the hexagon has 6 lines of symmetry; the large trapezoid has 1 line of symmetry; and each of the rhombuses has 2 lines

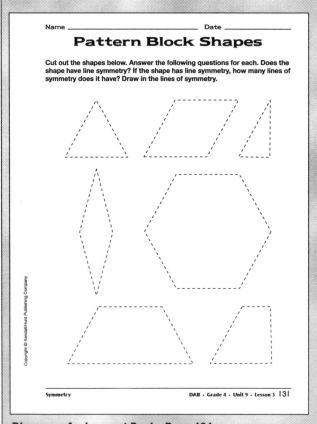

Discovery Assignment Book - Page 131

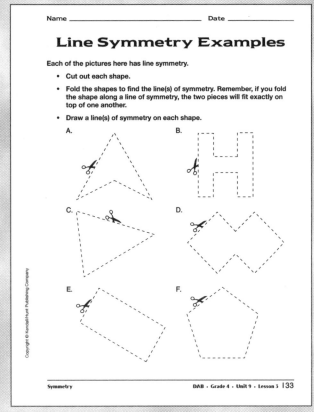

Line Symmetry Examples

Each of the pictures here has line symmetry.

- Cut out each shape.
- Fold the shapes to find the line(s) of symmetry. Remember, if you fold the shape along a line of symmetry, the two pieces will fit exactly on top of one another.
- Draw a line(s) of symmetry on each shape.

A.

B.

C.

D.

E.

F.

Discovery Assignment Book - Page 133

Content Note

The diagonals of shape E, the rectangle, are not lines of symmetry, even though they cut the rectangle into two congruent pieces.

TIMS Tip

Due to the thickness of their pencil point, students might have trouble tracing neatly around the pattern blocks. Have students mark a point on the paper at each vertex of the rhombus. Then, after removing the pattern block, students can connect the vertices with a ruler.

of symmetry. Place a transparency of the *Pattern Block Shapes* Activity Page on the overhead. After students discover which shapes have line symmetry, ask student volunteers to bring their cutouts up to the overhead. The students can mark the line(s) of symmetry for each shape on the transparency. Students can store their cutouts in an envelope.

Students then look at other figures and explore their symmetries. Have students work in pairs to complete the *Line Symmetry Examples* Activity Page in the *Discovery Assignment Book*. To identify whether a shape has line symmetry, students cut out the shape and try to fold it into two matching halves. Suggest that students use a ruler to draw the lines of symmetry along the fold lines. This page can be assigned for homework.

Part 2. Turn (Rotational) Symmetry

Students begin this exploration of turn symmetry by making a design that has turn symmetry. Remind students that a complete turn about a circle is 360 degrees. Distribute a blue rhombus pattern block to each student along with a blank sheet of paper. Ask students to mark a dot near the middle of a sheet of paper. This dot will be the center of turning for the first picture.

Tell students to place the rhombus on the paper so that a narrow vertex of the block is touching the center of turning. Ask students to trace the rhombus carefully. Illustrate this on the overhead or blackboard.

Now have the children turn the rhombus, pivoting about the center of turning so that one edge of the rhombus is on one of the traced lines. The vertex of the rhombus should still be touching the center of turning. Ask the children to trace the rhombus again. This time, they need only trace three of the sides, since one side is already traced. Their papers should look similar to Figure 21.

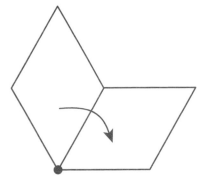

Figure 21: *Tracing a shape about the center of turning*

Tell children to continue turning and tracing until they have gone completely around in a circle. Their completed pictures should look like Figure 22.

Discuss the completed figure with your students. Ask them to determine the measure of the angle that they turned each time they turned the pattern block. This angle is called the **angle of turning.** They may measure or realize that the angle must be 60 degrees, since six of them complete a circle—6 × 60° = 360°. Encourage students to use a calculator to verify that 360 ÷ 6 = 60. If some students have difficulty seeing this, do not dwell on it but rather continue with the next example. They will eventually see the connection.

Ask students to use the tan rhombus, again with the narrow angle as the angle of turning. On a new sheet of paper, have students mark a center of turning. Have the students trace the rhombus and then turn the rhombus through the center of turning as shown in Figure 23. Continue until the tan rhombus has traveled a complete circle.

Discuss the figure formed with the class. The children should discover that the angle of turning is 30 degrees. Since 12 × 30 is 360, the tan rhombus, using the narrow angle, fits exactly 12 times around the center of turning. Use calculators to verify that 360 degrees ÷ 12 = 30 degrees.

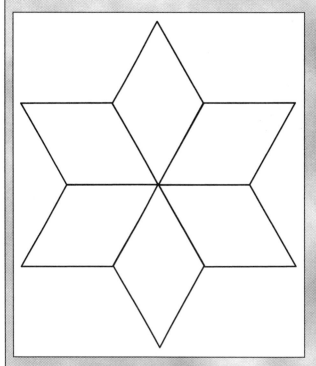

Figure 22: *Completed figure*

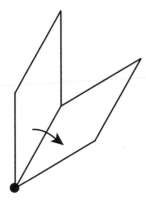

Figure 23: *Tracing a different shape*

Compare the figure created from the blue rhombus to the one created from the tan rhombus. Tell students that these two figures have **turn symmetry.** Symmetry in a figure means that a part of the shape can be traced and moved to lie on another part of the shape exactly. Figures that have turn symmetry have a **center of turning.** If a figure has **turn symmetry,** the figure when turned about the center of turning will coincide with itself after a turn that is less than 360°. The **type of turn symmetry** a figure has is the number of times the figure coincides with itself in making a complete circle. Since the design in Figure 22 coincides with

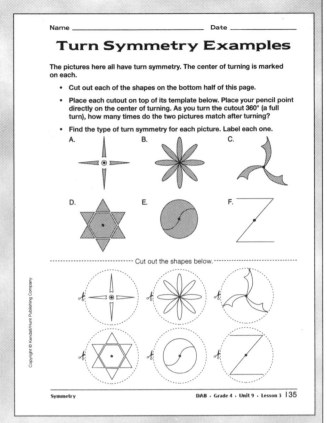

Turn Symmetry Examples

The pictures here all have turn symmetry. The center of turning is marked on each.

- Cut out each of the shapes on the bottom half of this page.
- Place each cutout on top of its template below. Place your pencil point directly on the center of turning. As you turn the cutout 360° (a full turn), how many times do the two pictures match after turning?
- Find the type of turn symmetry for each picture. Label each one.

A.　　　　B.　　　　C.

D.　　　　E.　　　　F.

------- Cut out the shapes below. -------

Symmetry　　　　　DAB · Grade 4 · Unit 9 · Lesson 3　135

Discovery Assignment Book - Page 135

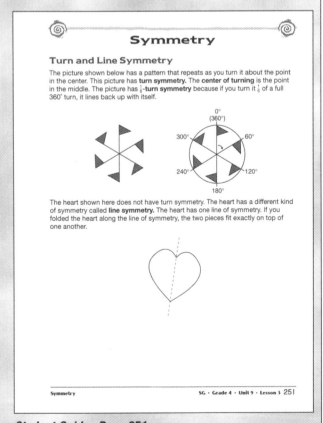

Symmetry

Turn and Line Symmetry

The picture shown below has a pattern that repeats as you turn it about the point in the center. This picture has **turn symmetry**. The **center of turning** is the point in the middle. The picture has $\frac{1}{6}$-**turn symmetry** because if you turn it $\frac{1}{6}$ of a full 360° turn, it lines back up with itself.

The heart shown here does not have turn symmetry. The heart has a different kind of symmetry called **line symmetry**. The heart has one line of symmetry. If you folded the heart along the line of symmetry, the two pieces fit exactly on top of one another.

Symmetry　　　　　SG · Grade 4 · Unit 9 · Lesson 3　251

Student Guide - Page 251

itself 6 times it has 6-fold symmetry. We also call this $\frac{1}{6}$-turn symmetry since each 60° turn is $\frac{1}{6}$ of a complete turn. 6 turns at 60° each is 360°—a complete turn.

Ask students to refer to the designs they created with the tan rhombus. Ask them to identify what type of turn symmetry this design has. The figure formed from the tan rhombus, using the narrow angle, has $\frac{1}{12}$-turn symmetry or 12-fold symmetry. Each 30° is $\frac{1}{12}$ of a complete turn. 12 turns at 30° each is 360° —a complete turn.

During this discussion of turn symmetry, make sure it is clear to students that it is the designs they are drawing that you are talking about, not the pattern blocks used to draw the designs. Students may confuse the two and think that it is the blue rhombus that has a $\frac{1}{6}$-turn symmetry and that the tan rhombus has a $\frac{1}{12}$-turn symmetry. This is not correct. Both of these pattern blocks have a $\frac{1}{2}$-turn symmetry.

As students investigate turn symmetry, you might want to remind them of line symmetry by asking if each shape they create also has line symmetry. The design made with blue rhombuses has six lines of symmetry, the design made with tan rhombuses has twelve.

Ask students to use the red trapezoid to create another figure that has turn symmetry. On a new sheet of paper, have the students mark a center of turning. Use the narrower, base angle as the angle of turning. See Figure 24.

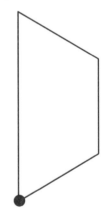

Figure 24: *Using the red trapezoid*

Have students trace the red trapezoid and then turn about the center of turning. Continue until the red trapezoid has traveled a complete circle. Ask:

- *Analyze the design you have drawn and determine the type of turn symmetry and the degree measure of the angle of turning.* (The completed pattern, shown in Figure 25, has $\frac{1}{6}$-turn symmetry or 6-fold symmetry. The angle of turning is 60°. Note that this design does not have line symmetry.)

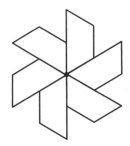

Figure 25: *Completed figure*

Refer to the large square you used in Part 1 of this lesson as well as the pattern block shapes on a transparency of the *Pattern Block Shapes* Activity Page. Ask students:

- *Which of these shapes have line symmetry?* (square, hexagon, equilateral triangle, large trapezoid, and both rhombuses)

First, punch a hole in one corner of the large paper square. The hole will be used here simply to mark one corner, not to change the shape. Place the square on the overhead. Place your pencil point in the center of the square holding the cutout in place. Then, with your other hand, turn the square 90° so that the square coincides once again with the square template. Before a full turn is completed (the punched hole returns to the original corner), the square coincides with the template 4 times as the square turns. The square has $\frac{1}{4}$-turn symmetry or 4-fold symmetry.

Now, use a transparency of the *Pattern Block Shapes* Activity Page and the cutouts of the transparent shapes to illustrate which of the pattern blocks have turn symmetry. First lay the *Pattern Block Shapes* transparency on the overhead as a template. Place the transparent square cutout on top of the square template. Draw a dot in the corner and repeat the procedure you used for the large paper square. Ask student volunteers to come up to the overhead to identify which other pattern block shapes have turn symmetry. If the shapes have turn symmetry, students should identify the center of turning. The following shapes have turn symmetry: hexagon ($\frac{1}{6}$-turn symmetry), equilateral triangle ($\frac{1}{3}$-turn symmetry), blue rhombus ($\frac{1}{2}$-turn symmetry), and the tan rhombus ($\frac{1}{2}$-turn symmetry).

TIMS Tip

Color each pattern block cutout with an overhead marker. Mark a corner with a dot. As you rotate each figure on top of the template, students will see whether the figure comes to rest on itself before you have gone about a complete turn.

Have students work in pairs to complete the *Turn Symmetry Examples* Activity Page in the *Discovery Assignment Book*. To identify the type of turn

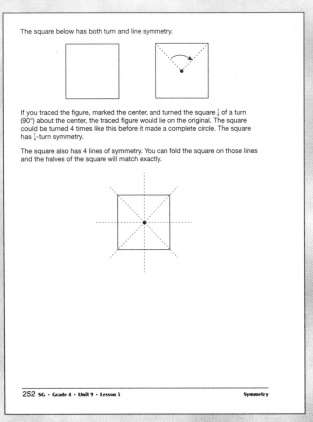

Student Guide - Page 252

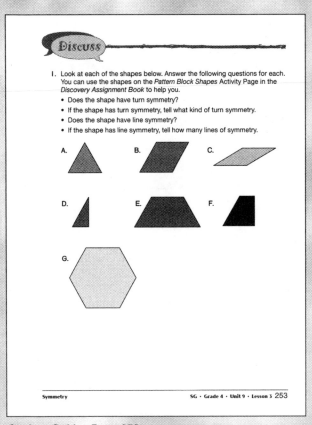

Student Guide - Page 253

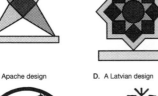

2. Many cultures use symmetry in their designs. Describe the symmetries you see in the following designs.

A. A design from ancient Pompeii (Roman Empire)

B. An Arabian design

C. An Apache design

D. A Latvian design

Student Guide - Page 254

Making Spinners

The idea of turn symmetry is seen in many places; for example, in spinners used for games.

The workers at the TIMS Toy Company are designing spinners for board games. Here is a spinner they designed for a game that is divided into 3 equal pieces. When children play the game, there is an equal chance of the spinner landing on any of the 3 areas.

For Questions 3 and 4, you will need the *Blank Spinners* Activity Page in the *Discovery Assignment Book*, a protractor, and a calculator. Answer these questions after creating your spinners:

- How big is the angle in each part of the spinner? Use your protractor to measure.
- What is the sum of all the angles? Does this make sense? Explain.

3. Design a spinner that is divided into 4 equal pieces. Explain your work.

4. Design a spinner that is divided into 5 equal pieces. Explain your work.

Student Guide - Page 255

---

symmetry, students are asked to cut out shapes and turn them about the center of turning.

At this point in the lesson, have students read the Turn and Line Symmetry section of the *Symmetry* Activity Pages in the *Student Guide*. **Question 1** reviews students' work with the pattern blocks and the *Pattern Block Shapes* transparencies. The shapes in **Question 2** from the Roman, Arabian, Apache, and Latvian cultures illustrate both line and turn symmetry. Discuss the symmetries students see in these designs.

Part 3. Making Spinners

We often use spinners in games in *Math Trailblazers*. If you have a spinner from a game, discuss it with your class. Discuss the divisions on a game spinner. For example, a game spinner might be divided into six equal regions and labeled 1, 2, 3, 4, 5, and 6. If the regions are equal, this means you have an equal chance of spinning any of the numbers 1–6.

Have students turn to the Making Spinners section in the *Student Guide* as well as the *Blank Spinners* Activity Page in the *Discovery Assignment Book*. Read together the introduction and directions in the *Student Guide*. Encourage students to use calculators and protractors to make their spinners. For **Questions 3–4**, students must divide spinners into equal regions. For **Question 3**, each region should measure 90°. In **Question 4**, 72° angles are needed to make the regions equal. Students will use spinners in their study of probability in Unit 14.

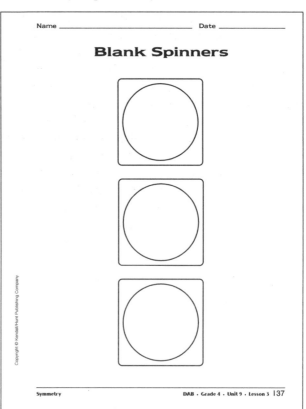

Discovery Assignment Book - Page 137

Suggestions for Teaching the Lesson

Homework and Practice

- The *Line Symmetry Examples* Activity Page in the *Discovery Assignment Book* may be assigned for homework.

- Assign the *More Symmetry* Homework Page in the *Discovery Assignment Book*.

- Use DPP item G to practice mental math for addition and subtraction problems. Task H presents data to be used to solve a logic puzzle. Task J asks students to estimate the size of angles.

- Home Practice Part 3 provides practice with addition, subtraction, and multiplication.

Answers for Part 3 of the Home Practice can be found at the end of this lesson and the end of this unit.

Assessment

- Use DPP item I as a quiz to assess students' abilities to identify types of angles and shapes.

- Use the *Observational Assessment Record* to document students' abilities to identify line and turn symmetry.

Daily Practice and Problems: Tasks for Lesson 3

H. Task: Whose Is Whose? (URG p. 17)

After gym class, Ms. Lyons asked Maya, Irma, and Linda to check the lost and found. They found a green glove, baseball hat, and jacket. Each girl had lost one item.

Use the clues below to determine who lost which item.

Clue A: Irma and Linda went to the lost and found together. One of them claimed the baseball hat and the other claimed the green glove.

Clue B: The green glove was not Irma's.

J. Task: Estimating Angles (URG p. 18)

Refer to the drawing. Tell whether the given angle is acute, obtuse, right, or 180°. Estimate the size of the angle in degrees. Think of a right angle and a 180° angle as references.

1. ∠BED
2. ∠BEC
3. ∠AEB
4. ∠CED
5. ∠DEA

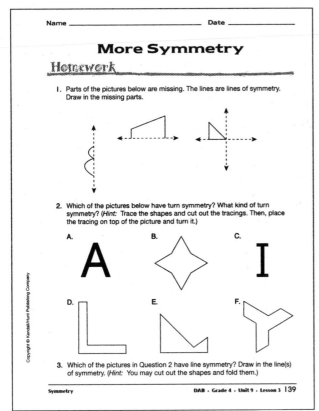

Name _____ Date _____

More Symmetry

Homework

1. Parts of the pictures below are missing. The lines are lines of symmetry. Draw in the missing parts.

2. Which of the pictures below have turn symmetry? What kind of turn symmetry? (*Hint:* Trace the shapes and cut out the tracings. Then, place the tracing on top of the picture and turn it.)

A. B. C.

D. E. F.

3. Which of the pictures in Question 2 have line symmetry? Draw in the line(s) of symmetry. (*Hint:* You may cut out the shapes and fold them.)

Symmetry   DAB · Grade 4 · Unit 9 · Lesson 3 139

Name _____ Date _____

Part 3 Addition, Subtraction, and Multiplication

1. Find the missing numbers needed to make these addition and subtraction problems correct. Use pencil and paper only.

A.	189	B.	322	C.	5078
	+ _____		− _____		+ _____
	612		284		8079

D.	7339	E.	5405	F.	3000
	− _____		+ _____		− _____
	6079		13,053		1456

2. Estimate the following products using convenient numbers. Write a number sentence to show your thinking.

   A. 290 × 18 =   B. 505 × 59 =   C. 9956 × 9 =

3. Find the products using paper and pencil or mental math. Be sure to estimate to make sure your answers are reasonable.

   A. 63 × 4 =   B. 37 × 8 =   C. 28 × 9 =

   D. 84 × 4 =   E. 66 × 3 =   F. 72 × 6 =

124 DAB · Grade 4 · Unit 9   SHAPES AND SOLIDS

Discovery Assignment Book - Page 139

Discovery Assignment Book - Page 124

AT A GLANCE

Math Facts and Daily Practice and Problems

Use mental math to solve addition and subtraction problems in DPP item G. Task H presents a logic problem. Bit I provides practice identifying angles and shapes. Task J practices estimating sizes of angles.

Part 1. Line (Reflective) Symmetry

1. Use a large paper square to illustrate one of the lines of symmetry in a square. Fold the square in half, unfold it, and mark the line of symmetry with a marker.
2. Ask student volunteers to find the three other lines of symmetry in the square.
3. Students cut out the shapes on the *Pattern Block Shapes* Activity Page in the *Discovery Assignment Book* and determine which of the shapes have line symmetry.
4. Student volunteers draw the lines of symmetry on the transparency of the *Pattern Block Shapes* Activity Page.
5. Student pairs complete the *Line Symmetry Examples* Activity Page in the *Discovery Assignment Book.*

Part 2. Turn (Rotational) Symmetry

1. Students trace the blue rhombus around in a circle, using the narrow angle as the center of turning.
2. Discuss the design created with the blue rhombus, including center of turning, angle of turning (60°), and type of symmetry ($\frac{1}{6}$-turn symmetry).
3. Repeat these steps using the narrow angle of the tan rhombus. The angle of turning is 30° and the type of symmetry is $\frac{1}{12}$-turn symmetry.
4. Repeat these steps using the narrow angle of the red trapezoid. The angle of turning is 60°.
5. Use the large paper square to demonstrate turn symmetry on the overhead.
6. Using the *Pattern Block Shapes* transparency and cutouts from a second transparency, students investigate which shapes have turn symmetry.
7. Student pairs complete the *Turn Symmetry Examples* Activity Page in the *Discovery Assignment Book.*
8. Students read the *Symmetry* Activity Pages in the *Student Guide.* Discuss *Questions 1–2.*

AT A GLANCE

Part 3. Making Spinners

1. Read together directions on the Making Spinners section in the *Student Guide*.
2. *Questions 3–4* in the *Student Guide* ask students to divide the regions on two spinners equally.

Homework

1. Assign the *More Symmetry* Homework Page in the *Discovery Assignment Book*.
2. Assign Home Practice Part 3 which provides computation problems.

Assessment

1. Use DPP item I as a quiz on identifying types of angles and shapes.
2. Observe students' abilities to identify line and turn symmetry. Record your observations on the *Observational Assessment Record*.

Notes:

Student Guide

Questions 1–4 (SG pp. 253–255)

1. **A.** The shape has $\frac{1}{3}$-turn symmetry and 3 lines of symmetry.

   B. $\frac{1}{2}$-turn symmetry and 2 lines of symmetry.

   C. $\frac{1}{2}$-turn symmetry and 2 lines of symmetry.

   D. No turn symmetry and no line symmetry.

   E. No turn symmetry and 1 line of symmetry.

   F. No turn symmetry and no line symmetry.

   G. $\frac{1}{6}$-turn symmetry and 6 lines of symmetry.

2. **A.** The design (including the rectangles at the top and bottom) has $\frac{1}{2}$-turn symmetry and two lines of symmetry. Without the rectangles, the pinwheel portion has $\frac{1}{4}$-turn symmetry and 4 lines of symmetry.

   B. The design (including the rectangles at the top and bottom) has $\frac{1}{2}$-turn symmetry and two lines of symmetry. Without the rectangles, it has $\frac{1}{8}$-turn symmetry and 8 lines of symmetry.

   C. The design has $\frac{1}{5}$-turn symmetry and 5 lines of symmetry.

   D. The design has $\frac{1}{4}$-turn symmetry and 4 lines of symmetry.

3. *Sum of angles is 360°.

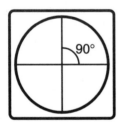

4. *Sum of angles is 360°.

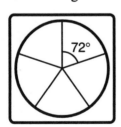

Discovery Assignment Book

**Home Practice (DAB p. 124)

Part 3. Addition, Subtraction, and Multiplication

Questions 1–3

1. **A.** 423

   B. 38

   C. 3001

   D. 1260

   E. 7648

   F. 1544

2. Answers will vary. Possible answers include:

   A. $300 \times 20 = 6000$

   B. $500 \times 60 = 30,000$

   C. $10,000 \times 9 = 90,000$

3. **A.** 252

   B. 296

   C. 252

   D. 336

   E. 198

   F. 432

---

*Answers and/or discussion are included in the Lesson Guide.

**Answers for all the Home Practice in the *Discovery Assignment Book* are at the end of the unit.

Pattern Block Shapes (DAB p. 131)

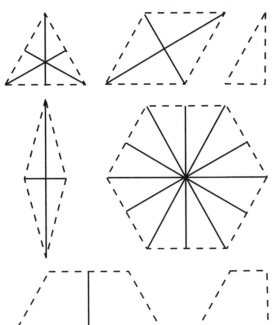

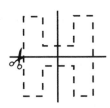

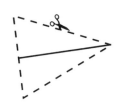

D.

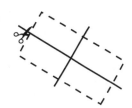

E.

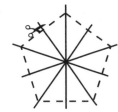

F.

Turn Symmetry Examples (DAB p. 135)

Questions A–F

A. $\frac{1}{4}$-turn symmetry
B. $\frac{1}{8}$-turn symmetry
C. $\frac{1}{3}$-turn symmetry
D. $\frac{1}{6}$-turn symmetry
E. $\frac{1}{2}$-turn symmetry
F. $\frac{1}{2}$-turn symmetry

Line Symmetry Examples* (DAB p. 133)

Questions A–F

A.

B.

C.

*Answers and/or discussion are included in the Lesson Guide.

**Answers for all the Home Practice in the *Discovery Assignment Book* are at the end of the unit.

More Symmetry (DAB p. 139)

Questions 1–3

1.

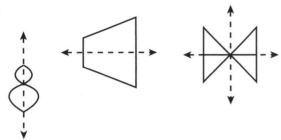

3. A.   B.   C.

   D.   E.   F.

2. **A.** no turn symmetry

   B. $\frac{1}{4}$-turn symmetry

   C. $\frac{1}{2}$-turn symmetry

   D. no turn symmetry

   E. no turn symmetry

   F. $\frac{1}{3}$-turn symmetry

*Answers and/or discussion are included in the Lesson Guide.

**Answers for all the Home Practice in the *Discovery Assignment Book* are at the end of the unit.

LESSON GUIDE 4

Journey to Flatopia

Estimated Class Sessions: 1

Students explore two- and three-dimensional worlds in a story about Professor Peabody and his adventures traveling in a two-dimensional world.

Key Content

• Exploring two and three dimensions.

Key Vocabulary

dimensions   sides
polygon   symmetry
rectangle   vertices
regular

OPTIONAL LESSON

There are no Daily Practice and Problems items for this lesson.

Materials List

Print Materials for Students

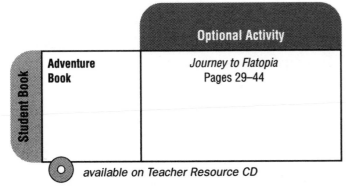

	Optional Activity
Adventure Book	*Journey to Flatopia* Pages 29–44

◉ *available on Teacher Resource CD*

All Transparency Masters, Blackline Masters, and Assessment Blackline Masters in the Unit Resource Guide are on the Teacher Resource CD.

Developing the Activity

We recommend that students read the story before any discussion. Then, choose discussion prompts that match your students' interests. This story can be used to challenge students' thinking about two and three dimensions.

Adventure Book - Page 30

Adventure Book - Page 31

Discussion Prompts

Page 30

- *The figure to the right of Professor Peabody is Mr. Origin, a figure that was used in Grades 1–3 to locate objects using coordinates.*

A volvox is a kind of small fresh-water organism with an interesting shape.

Page 31

Mr. Origin was used in third grade to make maps.

- *Who discovered zero?*

There is an Adventure Book, *The Nameless Scribe*, in third grade about the discovery of zero.

Discussion Prompts

Page 32

- *What is Sweet P. doing?*

Pressing the two-dimension button.

Use the surface of the overhead to demonstrate one, two, and three dimensions. Place a three-dimensional object such as a cube on the overhead, draw a square, and draw a line. Point out how each of the dimensions appears differently. (You may need to tip the cube a bit so students can see shadows of other sides.)

Content Note

Dimensions. Professor Peabody, you, me, cubes, books, houses—objects in the real world are three-dimensional (3-D) objects. Shapes and pictures you draw on a piece of paper such as squares, hexagons, etc., are all two-dimensional (2-D) objects. Lines are one-dimensional (1-D). Many people believe that the fourth dimension is time.

Page 35

- *What shape has four equal sides and four right angles?*

A square.

- *Does it have to be a square?*

Yes.

- *What shape has three sides of equal length?*

It is called an **equilateral triangle.** Equilateral means "equal sides" coming from the roots "equi" meaning equal and "lateral" meaning side.

- *What do you think a "lateral pass" is in football?*

When you pass to the side instead of forward.

Adventure Book - Page 32

Adventure Book - Page 35

The shape spoke to me once more. "I am Isabel Newton, head scientist of Flatopia. My mathematical theories predicted that there could be a three-dimensional world, but everyone in Flatopia thinks my theories are crazy. I was banished from Flatopia for teaching my students about three and four dimensions."

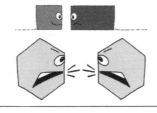

"Why are the beings here so afraid of me?" I asked.

"All living things in Flatopia are polygons," she said. "Flatopia beings think beauty is symmetry—the more lines of symmetry, the more beautiful. Also we think that the more vertices you have, the more important you are. You appear to have no vertices at all, and your sides are not line segments. Flatopians think you are very strange and ugly."

Dr. Newton then went on to tell me about Flatopia society. If two beings meet on the street, each one moves around the other and counts its vertices. The one with fewer vertices must move aside to let the other one pass. When both beings have the same number of vertices, the one with fewer lines of symmetry must move out of the way. For example, a nonsquare rectangle will have to move out of the way of a square. If two beings with the same number of sides and lines of symmetry meet, they will often have a nasty quarrel about who has the right of way.

36   AB · Grade 4 · Unit 9 · Lesson 4

Adventure Book - Page 36

Discussion Prompts

Page 36

• *How many lines of symmetry does Dr. Newton have?*

Six.

Dr. Newton is important and beautiful since she is a regular polygon (more specifically, a regular hexagon). **Regular** means all sides equal and all angles equal.

Here is a question that might come up in discussion of Flatopia or you may choose to bring it up if children seem curious.

• *How do the creatures in Flatopia see and what do they see? How do we see?*

Our eyes take in rays of light that come from or bounce off the object we look at. Our view of Flatopia is a view from the three-dimensional world, outside of Flatopia. For example, we can see all six of Dr. Newton's sides at once. But Professor Peabody in Flatopia would only see three sides of Dr. Newton. See Figure 26.

Figure 26: *Professor Peabody's view*

• *What would Dr. Newton look like to Professor Peabody?*

You can get an idea of this by putting a hexagonal pattern block on a table. While looking at the pattern block, gradually move your head down until you are level with the table. Imagine you are moving into Flatopia, i.e., the surface of the table. Now you can only see the three sides of the hexagonal pattern block that are closest to you.

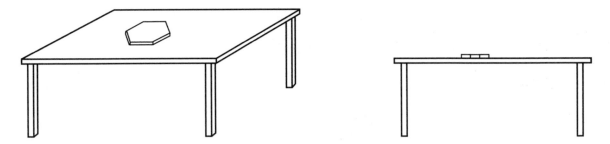

Figure 27: *Looking at it from another view*

This is still not Flatopia, since the shapes in Flatopia have no thickness. So imagine the pattern block getting thinner and thinner. What you are finally left with is yellow line segments! So the world "looks like" lines to the inhabitants of Flatopia, and different objects look like line segments. Color is a big help in telling one object from another.

• *How many lines of symmetry does a square have?*

Four.

• *How many lines of symmetry does a nonsquare rectangle have?*

Two.

• *Why does a nonsquare rectangle have to get out of the way for a square?*

A square has more lines of symmetry than a nonsquare rectangle.

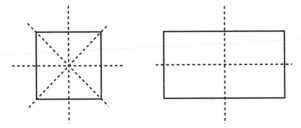

Figure 28: *Lines of symmetry in a square and a rectangle*

• *Why do we say "nonsquare rectangle"?*

Because a square is a rectangle. A **rectangle** can be defined to be any quadrilateral with four right angles. Many children believe that a square is not a rectangle. This is probably due, at least partly, to being asked which one is a square and which one is a rectangle when shown a picture of a square and a (nonsquare) rectangle.

All the farmers in Flatopia are right triangles. There are two kinds of right triangles, left-facing triangles (called Lefties) and right-facing triangles (called Righties).

Welcome to Triangle Family Feud!
Now ... Let's meet our Feuding Families ...

Mr. & Mrs. Hugo Left & Family

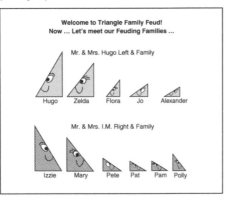

Hugo   Zelda   Flora   Jo   Alexander

Mr. & Mrs. I.M. Right & Family

Izzie   Mary   Pete   Pat   Pam   Polly

For centuries, the Righties and Lefties have been feuding. Since they are always fighting, they do not spend enough time growing crops. Now there is a food shortage in Flatopia. Strangely enough, no one remembers how this feud began and no one can think of a way to end it.

Adventure Book - Page 37

As Dr. Newton was explaining this to me, I noticed that some beings were approaching us. After feeling their sides and vertices, I could tell that they were all squares. "Horrible creature," they said to me, "His Majesty King Deka X commands that you stop speaking with the troublemaker, Dr. Newton, and come immediately to his castle." This was said in a most unfriendly tone, so I began to worry about my safety.

"King Deka thinks he is the most powerful and symmetric person in the world," said Dr. Newton. "He has the largest number of sides in the kingdom, 10, and is a regular polygon. So he has 10 lines of symmetry." "Stop talking to this creature, Dr. Newton," said the captain of the squares. "You've made enough trouble already, filling people's heads with fairy tales about a three-dimensional world. Clap them in chains!" With this command, I was surrounded by squares and Dr. Newton and I were escorted to the royal court.

As soon as the captain told the king about my arrival and my conversation with Dr. Newton, the king shouted, "Off with his head! Heretics must be punished!" "But, Your Majesty," I shouted, "I can prove that there is a three-dimensional world." The queen turned to the king and said, "This creature is amusing. Let's hear what it has to say, dear." "Hrrumph!" grumbled the king. "Let the madman speak."

"Most wise King," I said, "since your world is two-dimensional, you cannot see a three-dimensional object." "Obviously," replied the king. "Now," I said, "I will show a three-dimensional object called a sphere, but we will only be able to see two-dimensional slices called circles."

Adventure Book - Page 38

Discussion Prompts

Page 37

Students are sometimes confused by the two uses of the word right. A right triangle is a triangle with a 90 degree angle (also called a right angle). This is similar to the use of right as a suffix in the word "upright." On the other hand, right is a direction, the opposite of left. The right- and left-facing "right triangles" are introduced in this story to make the point that a right-facing right triangle cannot be moved so that it is a left-facing right triangle if it stays within the plane (i.e., Flatopia). But when you reflect, going out of the plane (Flatopia), then right-facing triangles become left-facing triangles. This happens on page 42 of the Adventure Book.

Page 38

Deka is the Greek prefix meaning ten. You could say that King Deka is a decagon.

- *How do you know that a regular decagon has 10 lines of symmetry?*

There is one line of symmetry through the midpoints of each pair of opposite sides (that makes 5 lines of symmetry) and one line of symmetry through each pair of opposite vertices. See Figure 29, which shows the lines of symmetry of an octagon. Every regular polygon with an even number of sides has as many lines of symmetry as sides. Can you see why?

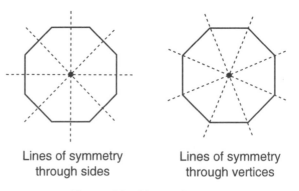

Lines of symmetry   Lines of symmetry
through sides   through vertices

Figure 29: *Lines of symmetry*

Discussion Prompts

Page 39

One way to think about the sphere passing through Flatopia is to think that, at first, the Flatopians see the south pole of the sphere. Then, they see circles of latitude. The biggest one is the equator. Then they see lines of latitude in the northern hemisphere. The last thing they see is the north pole.

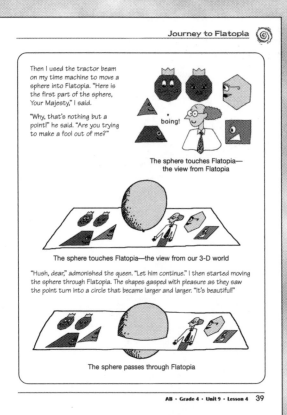

Adventure Book - Page 39

Page 40

Infinite means "more than any number" or "cannot be counted in a finite amount of time." For example, there are an infinite number of whole numbers, since you can never finish counting all of them.

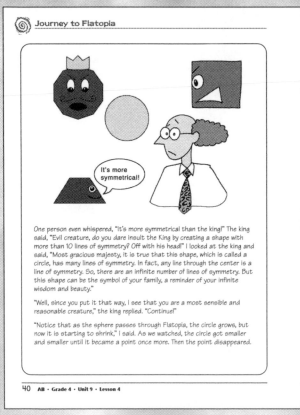

Student Guide - Page 40

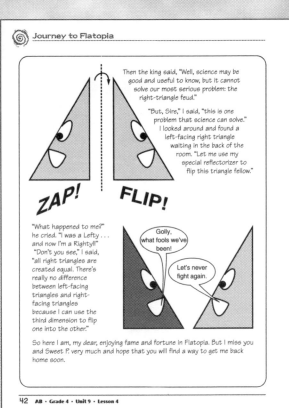

Adventure Book - Page 42

Page 42

- *What did Professor Peabody do with the special reflectorizer?*

Professor Peabody is using the reflectorizer to have the triangle flip over through three-dimensional space. You may want to demonstrate how Professor Peabody flipped the 2-D triangles over by moving them through 3-D space. Cut out a right triangle similar to the right triangle on the Adventure Book page. Show it on the overhead. Tell students that the surface of the overhead is Flatopia (2-D space). Flip the triangle over. Point out that a right-facing triangle becomes a left-facing triangle after it moves through 3-D space.

> ### 📓 Journal Prompt
> Write a story in which Professor Peabody and Sweet P. return to Flatopia and have further adventures. Among the things that they might find out are: what is the weather like in Flatopia, how do Flatopians grow vegetables, what jobs do various shapes have, and who are some other members of the royal family? Remember that all living things in Flatopia are polygons. Review Dr. Newton's description of Flatopia on page 36 before you begin writing your story.

LESSON GUIDE

Prisms

Estimated Class Sessions:
2–3

This lesson has four parts. In all four parts, students describe three-dimensional objects and their representation in two dimensions. In Part 1, students identify and count the edges, faces, and vertices of a box. They also sketch boxes. In Part 2, students cut boxes so they can flatten them out and describe the resulting net. Students reverse the process in Part 3. They make cubes from nets. They also analyze two-dimensional drawings and decide which are in fact nets of cubes (those that will form cubes). Finally, in Part 4, students discuss different types of prisms and build a triangular prism and a hexagonal prism from nets.

Key Content

- Making nets for three-dimensional shapes.
- Making shapes from nets.
- Visualizing a three-dimensional shape from a two-dimensional net.
- Identifying a net of a prism.
- Describing prisms using their properties.
- Drawing three-dimensional shapes.

Key Vocabulary

dimensions	prism
edge	rectangular prism
face	regular polygon
hexagonal prism	solid
net	vertex

Daily Practice and Problems: Bits for Lesson 5

K. More Fact Practice (URG p. 18)

Find n to make each number sentence true.

A. $8 \times 5 = n$ B. $n \times 7 = 70$

C. $n \div 4 = 5$ D. $80 \div n = 10$

E. $10 \times n = 50$ F. $30 \div 5 = n$

G. $9 \times 10 = n$ H. $15 \div n = 5$

I. $n \times 8 = 80$ J. $10 \div 10 = n$

M. More Fact Families for $\times$ and $\div$ (URG p. 20)

New uniforms for the cheerleading and pompom squads were delivered today at Oakland High. Each box contained 8 uniforms. If 40 uniforms were ordered in all, how many boxes arrived?

There are 5 groups of 8 in 40. Think: $? \times 8 = 40$ or $40 \div 8 = ?$

The answer to both questions is 5.

Solve the following problems. Each group of facts is related.

A. $10 \times 7 =$ $70 \div 7 =$
     $7 \times 10 =$ $70 \div 10 =$

B. $2 \times 5 =$ $10 \div 5 =$
     $5 \times 2 =$ $10 \div 2 =$

C. $6 \times 5 =$ $30 \div 5 =$
     $5 \times 6 =$ $30 \div 6 =$

DPP Challenges are on page 80. Suggestions for using the DPPs are on pages 80–81.

Curriculum Sequence

Before This Unit

In Grade 3 Unit 18, students described rectangular prisms using their properties and they learned to sketch cubes.

Materials List

Print Materials for Students

	Math Facts and Daily Practice and Problems	Activity	Homework
Student Guide		*Prisms* Pages 256–260	*Prisms* Homework Section Pages 260–262
Discovery Assignment Book		*Nets* Pages 141–143, *A Hexagonal Prism* Pages 145–147, and *Right Triangular Prism* Page 149	Home Practice Part 4 Page 125
Facts Resource Guide	DPP Items 9K & 9M		
Unit Resource Guide	DPP Items K–N Pages 18–21		

available on Teacher Resource CD

All Transparency Masters, Blackline Masters, and Assessment Blackline Masters in the Unit Resource Guide are on the Teacher Resource CD.

Supplies for Each Student

small cardboard box
transparent tape
scissors
protractor
ruler

Materials for the Teacher

Nets 1 Transparency Master (Unit Resource Guide) Page 83
Nets 2 Transparency Master (Unit Resource Guide) Page 84
extra paper copies of *Nets 1*, *Nets 2* Transparency Masters
extra copies of *A Hexagonal Prism* Activity Pages (Discovery Assignment Book) Pages 145–147
copy of *Right Triangular Prism* Activity Page (Discovery Assignment Book) Page 149
Observational Assessment Record (Unit Resource Guide, Pages 9–10 and Teacher Resource CD)
several rectangular solids or boxes, other than cubes
other examples of prisms (the wooden solids can be used here), optional
one or two medium-sized boxes (cereal boxes work well)

Before the Activity

Have students bring cereal boxes or other small boxes to class. If the top of the box was cut when it was used, the student should tape it together before the activity.

Collect some other shapes, including a cube. These can be used for Lesson 6 as well. A pack from the base-ten pieces is a cube. Collect several kinds of rectangular boxes. If possible, find boxes that have other shapes as bases. For example, some candies come in triangular and hexagonal boxes. Prisms made from other materials can be used as well. Nets for a right triangular prism and a hexagonal prism are provided in the *Discovery Assignment Book* to be used if needed.

Developing the Activity

Part 1. Exploring Boxes

Describing a Box (Prism). Show students a cereal or similar box. Each student should have a box as well. The box should be closed. Remind students that the box is a 3-dimensional shape or a **solid.** (Refer to the content note in Lesson 4 about **dimensions.**) The sides of a three-dimensional shape are called **faces.** Show children the **edges** and **vertices** (or corners) of the box. Your students may know that a box is a *rectangular prism.* Use this term to discuss boxes if it is familiar to the students.

Ask them to describe the faces of the box.

* *What is the shape of each face?* (rectangle)
* *Are any of the faces the same size and shape?* (The opposite faces are the same size and shape.)

Discuss *Questions 1–3* on the *Prisms* Activity Pages in the *Student Guide.* Students should see that there are 6 faces, 12 edges, and 8 vertices.

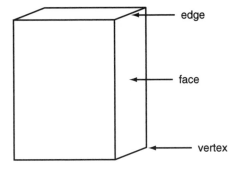

Figure 30: *A box that is a rectangular prism*

Content Note

You will note that a cereal box or the object that we create from a net is not actually solid (in the everyday sense of the word). It actually represents the surface of a solid. For simplicity, in this unit we often use the same word (for example, prism) to refer to a solid and the surface of a solid.

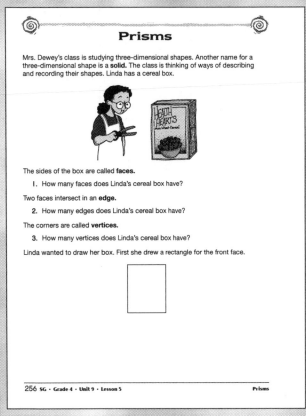

Prisms

Mrs. Dewey's class is studying three-dimensional shapes. Another name for a three-dimensional shape is a **solid.** The class is thinking of ways of describing and recording their shapes. Linda has a cereal box.

The sides of the box are called **faces.**

1. How many faces does Linda's cereal box have?

Two faces intersect in an **edge.**

2. How many edges does Linda's cereal box have?

The corners are called **vertices.**

3. How many vertices does Linda's cereal box have?

Linda wanted to draw her box. First she drew a rectangle for the front face.

Student Guide - Page 256

Drawing a Prism. Invite members of the class to explain how to draw a box (prism). Students should each have a box so that they can refer to the box as they attempt to sketch it. You may use cubes also. Students may know several methods of sketching boxes. Discuss these as a group.

One way to begin is by drawing the front face of the box. Above and to the right of the first rectangle, draw another rectangle of the same size as shown in Figure 31.

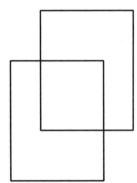

Figure 31: *Drawing a box*

Notice that a new rectangle is formed from the overlapping rectangles. Then, connect corresponding vertices.

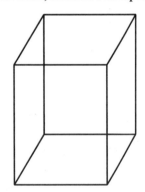

Figure 32: *A finished box*

Note to students that dashed lines are often used to indicate that an edge cannot be seen as in Figure 33.

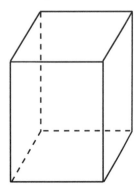

Figure 33: *Hidden edges of a box*

To get a more accurate drawing, a template of a rectangle can be used. Show students how to draw a rectangle with sides parallel to the sides of the paper using a clear ruler.

Another way to draw a box, discussed in the *Student Guide,* is again to begin with a rectangle. Using this method allows students to use parallel lines discussed in Lesson 1.

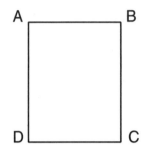

Figure 34: *Another method of drawing a box*

Now draw three parallel line segments of equal length. Call them $\overline{AE}$, $\overline{BF}$, and $\overline{CG}$. In Figure 35, each of the three segments is 2 cm long.

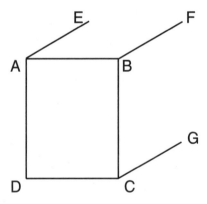

Figure 35: *Drawing parallel lines*

Draw $\overline{EF}$ and $\overline{FG}$ as shown in Figure 36.

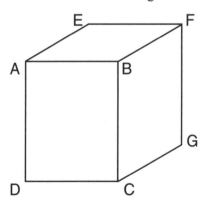

Figure 36: *Closing the box*

Finally, draw in $\overline{DH}$ parallel to $\overline{AE}$, $\overline{EH}$ parallel to $\overline{FG}$, and $\overline{HG}$ parallel to $\overline{EF}$.

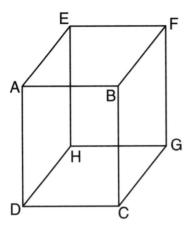

Figure 37: *Completing the drawing of a box*

The box shown in Figure 37 was drawn from a perspective that allows us to actually see three faces. When looking at a drawing, do the faces look like rectangles? Help students see that some of the faces appear to be parallelograms. Ask students to turn their boxes and ask whether they always see three faces. What other perspectives are possible? Guide students to see that it is possible to see only one face if you look at a box head on. Then, the drawing of the box is simply a rectangle as shown in Figure 38.

It is also possible to look at a box and see two faces as shown in Figure 39.

Figure 38: *A box viewed head on*

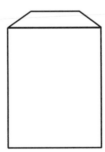

Figure 39: *Seeing two faces of a box*

Homework *Question 1* on the *Prisms* Activity Pages in the *Student Guide* can be assigned after this part of the lesson.

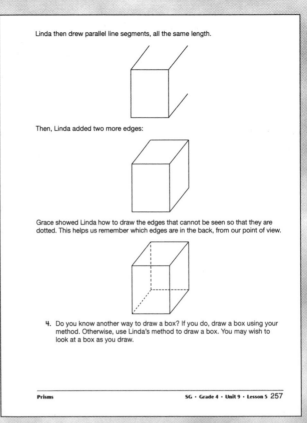

Linda then drew parallel line segments, all the same length.

Then, Linda added two more edges:

Grace showed Linda how to draw the edges that cannot be seen so that they are dotted. This helps us remember which edges are in the back, from our point of view.

4. Do you know another way to draw a box? If you do, draw a box using your method. Otherwise, use Linda's method to draw a box. You may wish to look at a box as you draw.

Prisms   SG · Grade 4 · Unit 9 · Lesson 5   257

Student Guide - Page 257

Content Note

Perspective. There are a number of different ways of drawing objects so that they look three-dimensional. Sometimes this is called perspective drawing. The dictionary definition of perspective is the art of drawing solid objects on a flat surface so that it produces the same impression as do the actual objects when viewed from a particular point.

Making Nets from Boxes

Linda was interested in the way boxes are made. She decided to flatten out her box. Linda decided to cut along three of the top edges and four of the vertical edges. This is what she got.

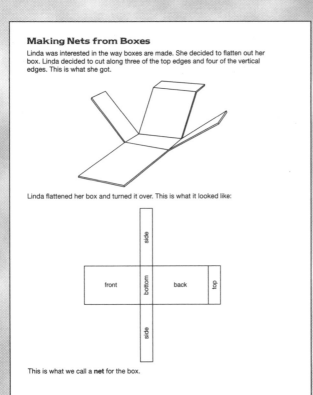

Linda flattened her box and turned it over. This is what it looked like:

	side		
front	bottom	back	top
	side		

This is what we call a **net** for the box.

258 SG · Grade 4 · Unit 9 · Lesson 5   Prisms

---

5. There are other ways to flatten a box. Work with your group to make as many different nets of a box as you can. Each person in the group should have a box to cut. Make one net at a time. Discuss before you cut so that you do not repeat a net.

6. Draw a picture of your nets. Label the rectangles that were the bottom, top, and sides of the box.

Different Kinds of Prisms

Boxes are examples of special kinds of three-dimensional shapes. These shapes are prisms.

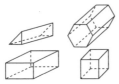

These shapes are not prisms.

A **prism** is a three-dimensional shape. Prisms have two identical faces called bases. The bases are parallel to each other. The other faces are parallelograms.

Prisms   SG · Grade 4 · Unit 9 · Lesson 5   259

TIMS Tip

When you open most cereal boxes, you are forced to split the top. In other words, the "cuts" you make to open the box are not made along the edges. To make a net, tape the two halves of the top together to make a rectangle before cutting the edges.

Part 2. Making Nets from Boxes

Read with students the Making Nets from Boxes section in the *Student Guide.* In this section, students explore how to flatten a box into a two-dimensional shape. *Question 5* asks children to cut along some of the edges in order to lay all the faces flat on the table and not destroy any of the faces. Also, the box is to remain in one piece. The object made by cutting a box (or any other three-dimensional shape whose faces are polygons) along its edges and flattening it out while preserving its faces is called a **net** for the box.

Have your students answer *Questions 5–6.* One way to get a greater variety of nets is to ask some groups to find nets with one vertical cut, other groups to use two vertical cuts, three vertical cuts, and the remaining groups to use four vertical cuts. You can also assign each group the task of finding a net with one vertical cut, two vertical cuts, etc. Students who work faster can find more than one "different" solution, provided there are enough boxes. Have students discuss which nets are really made in a different way. Figure 40 shows a number of different nets for the same box.

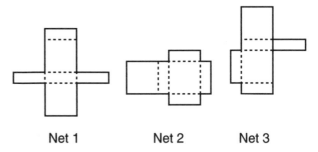

Net 1   Net 2   Net 3

Figure 40: *Some nets for the box in Figure 30*

Part 3. Nets

An overhead projector is strongly recommended for this part of the activity. However, it can be done without a projector by holding up the figures or taping them to an easel or blackboard.

Show the *Nets 1* Transparency Master to the class. Ask:

- *Can this figure be cut out and folded to make a closed three-dimensional shape?*
- *What would the shape look like?*

Through discussion students should conclude that this is a pattern or net of a cube. Encourage students to explain why this pattern will fold to make a cube. They may refer to certain squares of the net as the "bottom" or "sides" of the cube. Allow several students to verbalize their thinking. Use a cutout copy of the net to illustrate creasing and folding to make the cube. Use both the paper copy and the overhead copy to show where each square moves to become the final shape.

Show the *Nets 2* Transparency Master. Ask:

- *Are these two figures nets of cubes?*

Encourage them to explain their thinking. The class should come to the conclusion that Figure A is not a net of a cube, since when folded, two of the squares overlap. Figure B is, however, a net of a cube. Use cutout paper copies to help students visualize folding the nets.

Ask students to do **Questions 1–6** on the *Nets* Activity Pages in the *Discovery Assignment Book.* Students can work individually or in groups. You may also assign these as homework. Encourage students to cut out the shapes when needed. Discuss which patterns are nets of cubes and which are not. Encourage students to explain their thinking.

Homework **Questions 2–5** on the *Prisms* Activity Pages in the *Student Guide* can be assigned after this part of the lesson. These questions help students visualize three-dimensional objects from two-dimensional nets.

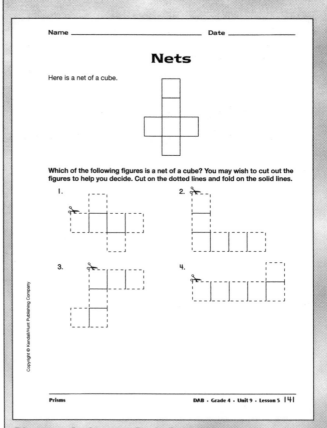

Discovery Assignment Book - Page 141

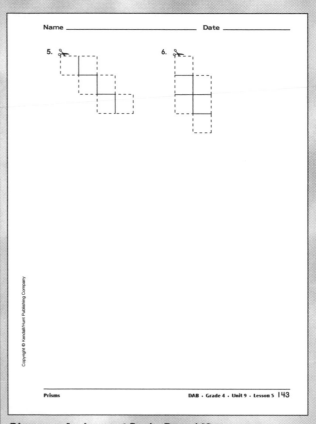

Discovery Assignment Book - Page 143

Discovery Assignment Book - Page 145

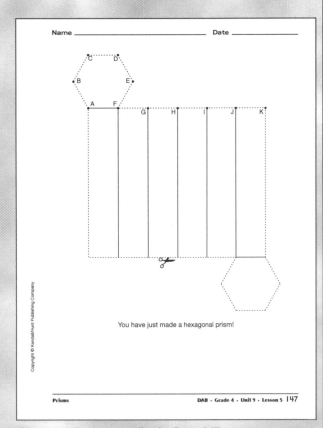

Discovery Assignment Book - Page 147

Part 4. Different Kinds of Prisms

Explain to students that most boxes are prisms. The **prisms** discussed here are three-dimensional solids with two bases and rectangular faces that connect the bases. It is possible to have prisms with parallelograms that are not rectangles as sides. Such prisms are no longer right prisms and are not covered here. The type of prism depends on the shape of the base. Cereal boxes are rectangular prisms. The base of a prism is a polygonal region. Figure 41 shows a triangular prism, rectangular prism, and hexagonal prism. These prisms are shown in the Different Kinds of Prisms section in the *Student Guide*.

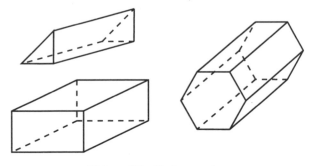

Figure 41: *Various prisms*

Ask students to complete ***Questions 1–6*** on *A Hexagonal Prism* Activity Pages in the *Discovery Assignment Book*. After students have completed the questions, discuss their answers together. Then, have students construct the hexagonal prism. Make sure everyone sees that the short sides of the rectangle are the same length as the sides of the hexagon. Note that these hexagons are special in that all the sides are equal in length and all the angles have equal measure. Recall that polygons with all sides and all angles equal are called *regular polygons*.

Have students make the prism on the *Right Triangular Prism* Activity Page in the *Discovery Assignment Book*.

TIMS Tip
Make sure students score the interior edges of their prisms using a sharp pencil and straightedge before folding if you are using heavier paper. Their prisms will be much neater and more attractive.

Display a variety of different prisms for the class to observe and explore. For example, you might use a hexagonal prism, a cereal box, a triangular prism, and any other prisms you have available. The wooden solids set, recommended in the materials list, contains several prisms.

Students should also use their hexagonal and right triangular prisms. These prisms should be saved for Lesson 6. Ask students to work in groups to answer the folowing:

- *How are all these prisms similar? Write down your answers.*
- *Count the number of faces on each solid.*

Students may notice, for example:

- The shapes consist of two bases and connecting rectangles.
- The number of rectangles is the number of sides of the base.
- The bases are parallel to one another.

Remind students that you discussed parallel lines in Lesson 1, that is, lines in two dimensions. If the bases of the prisms were extended, they too would never meet. We say the bases are parallel. The distance between the corresponding points on the bases are the same distance apart, since the rectangles that make up the sides of the prism are identical (congruent).

Content Note

A cube is a special kind of rectangular prism because a square is a special type of rectangle.

Content Note

Parallel lines need to be in the same plane. Lines in space can be skew lines. That is, the lines never meet but they are not parallel.

📓 Journal Prompt

Pick a prism. Describe in words what you see as you look at the prism from various perspectives (various angles).

Content Note

Solids, Polyhedra, and Prisms. Three-dimensional objects are called solids (or geometric solids). A **polyhedron** is a solid with all polygonal faces. **Prisms** are special kinds of polyhedra.

Rather than spending time dealing with the precise mathematical definition of a prism, we prefer that students get multiple experiences with a variety of prisms, develop an informal notion of what a prism is, and develop precise definitions when they are capable of higher-level geometric thinking. The most important features of prisms are that they have two polygonal faces that are the same size and shape (we can call these the bases, or the bottom and the top of the prism), and sides that are parallelograms. All of the prisms we will be using are, technically, right prisms. This means that the sides are, in fact, rectangles. But we will just use the term triangular prism instead of "right triangular prism." One way of classifying prisms is according to the shapes of their bases. Thus, the usual prism that is used in science to separate colors of light is a triangular prism and most cereal boxes are rectangular prisms.

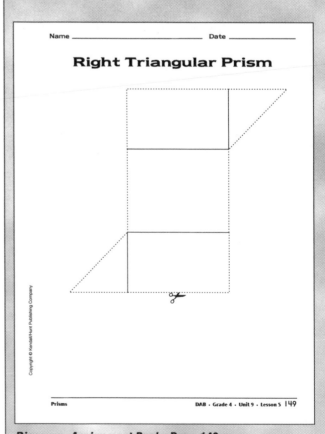

Name _____ Date _____

Right Triangular Prism

Prisms   DAB · Grade 4 · Unit 9 · Lesson 5 149

Discovery Assignment Book - Page 149

Daily Practice and Problems:
Challenges for Lesson 5

L. Challenge: Which Is Which?
(URG p. 19)

Nila, Grace, Tanya, and Lee Yah are in gymnastics class. Each girl is practicing on a different piece of equipment: balance beam, vault, trampoline, and uneven parallel bars.

Read the clues below to discover which girl is working on which piece of equipment.

Clue A: Nila and her friend who is on the balance beam are more advanced than Grace.

Clue B: Tanya and her friend who is on the trampoline are better at round-offs than Lee Yah and Grace.

Clue C: The girl on the vault and Grace both watched the Olympic gymnastic trials last Saturday on TV.

Clue D: Lee Yah is not on the balance beam.

N. Challenge: Parallel and Perpendicular (URG p. 21)

1. Draw a line segment on your paper and label the endpoints A and B.

2. Draw a line segment parallel to $\overline{AB}$ and label it $\overline{CD}$.

3. Draw a line segment, $\overline{EF}$, perpendicular to $\overline{AB}$ and intersecting $\overline{AB}$ and $\overline{CD}$.

4. Is $\overline{EF}$ also perpendicular to $\overline{CD}$? Why or why not?

5. Draw another line segment that is neither perpendicular nor parallel to any of the others.

6. Carefully erase your letters and show your drawing to a friend. Have him or her show you a pair of parallel lines and a pair of perpendicular lines.

Suggestions for Teaching the Lesson

Math Facts

DPP items K and M provide multiplication and division facts practice.

Homework and Practice

- Assign the Homework section in the *Student Guide*. *Question 1* can be assigned after Part 1 of the lesson. *Questions 2–5* can be assigned after Part 3. *Questions 6–12* can be assigned at the end of the lesson.

- Challenge N reviews drawing line segments and the concepts of parallel and perpendicular lines.

- Assign Home Practice Part 4 for practice reading clocks and solving problems involving elapsed time.

Answers for Part 4 of the Home Practice can be found in the Answer Key at the end of this lesson and at the end of this unit.

Assessment

- The homework in the *Student Guide* can be used to assess student understanding of nets and prisms.

- Use the *Observational Assessment Record* to note students' abilities to identify a net of a prism.

One way to sketch a prism is to draw the two bases and then connect the matching vertices. You may want to trace the bases from a picture, a pattern block, or some other object. Here is a way to draw a pentagonal prism:

You may wish to dot the lines that show the edges that are in the back of the figure. Prisms can be drawn with or without the dotted lines. Compare the drawing of the following pentagonal prism with the one above. Which one seems clearer to you?

7. How many faces does a pentagonal prism have? How many edges? How many vertices?

Homework

Boxes

1. Find a box at home. Make a sketch of the box showing its length, width, and height. You can measure using centimeters or inches.

For Questions 2–5, decide whether the figure is a net of a cube. You may need to trace the figures on a separate sheet of paper and cut them out.

2.

3.

Student Guide - Page 260

Extension

- Students can decorate the hexagonal and triangular prisms (and attach string) before they cut, fold, and tape the prism closed. Then, hang the prisms around the classroom.

- Have students draw several prisms. Begin by drawing the two bases and then connecting the corresponding vertices. Sketches of a triangular prism and an octagonal prism are shown in Figure 42. The *Student Guide* shows a way of sketching a pentagonal prism.

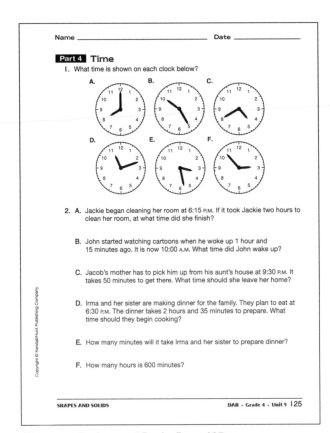

Figure 42: *A triangular prism and an octagonal prism*

- DPP Challenge L offers a logic puzzle.

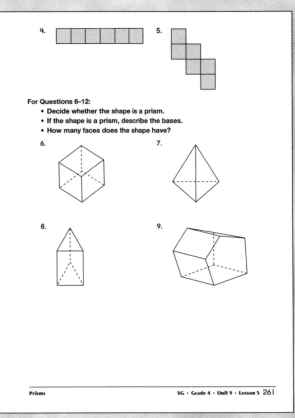

4. 5.

For Questions 6–12:
- Decide whether the shape is a prism.
- If the shape is a prism, describe the bases.
- How many faces does the shape have?

6. 7.

8. 9.

Student Guide - Page 261

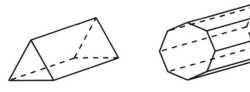

Name _____ Date _____

Part 4 Time

1. What time is shown on each clock below?

A. B. C.

D. E. F.

2. A. Jackie began cleaning her room at 6:15 P.M. If it took Jackie two hours to clean her room, at what time did she finish?

B. John started watching cartoons when he woke up 1 hour and 15 minutes ago. It is now 10:00 A.M. What time did John wake up?

C. Jacob's mother has to pick him up from his aunt's house at 9:30 P.M. It takes 50 minutes to get there. What time should she leave her home?

D. Irma and her sister are making dinner for the family. They plan to eat at 6:30 P.M. The dinner takes 2 hours and 35 minutes to prepare. What time should they begin cooking?

E. How many minutes will it take Irma and her sister to prepare dinner?

F. How many hours is 600 minutes?

Discovery Assignment Book - Page 125

10. 11.

12.

Student Guide - Page 262

AT A GLANCE

Math Facts and Daily Practice and Problems

DPP items K and M provide math facts practice. Item L challenges students with a logic puzzle. Item N reviews parallel and perpendicular lines.

Part 1. Exploring Boxes

1. Discuss the faces, edges, and vertices of a box using the *Prisms* Activity Pages in the *Student Guide.*
2. Discuss ways to sketch a box.
3. Discuss various perspectives of a box.

Part 2. Making Nets from Boxes

1. Demonstrate cutting a box along its edges to flatten it out.
2. Students cut their boxes along edges and flatten them out to make nets.
3. Students look for different solutions and sketch the nets they have made.

Part 3. Nets

1. Discuss whether the *Nets 1* Transparency Master in the *Unit Resource Guide* is a pattern for a cube.
2. Discuss the patterns shown on the *Nets 2* Transparency Master in the *Unit Resource Guide.*
3. Students do *Questions 1–6* on the *Nets* Activity Pages in the *Discovery Assignment Book.*

Part 4. Different Kinds of Prisms

1. Introduce the terminology for prisms. See the Different Kinds of Prisms section in the *Student Guide.*
2. Students construct a hexagonal and triangular prism using the *A Hexagonal Prism* and *Right Triangular Prism* Activity Pages in the *Discovery Assignment Book.*
3. Students discuss properties of prisms.

Homework

1. Students complete the homework questions in the *Student Guide: Question 1* after Part 1, *Questions 2–5* after Part 3, and *Questions 6–12* after Part 4.
2. Assign Part 4 of the Home Practice.

Assessment

Use the *Observational Assessment Record* to document students' abilities to identify the net of a prism.

Notes:

Nets 1

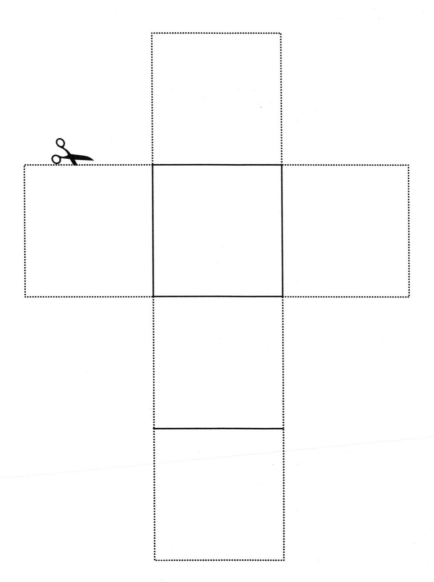

Nets 2

A.

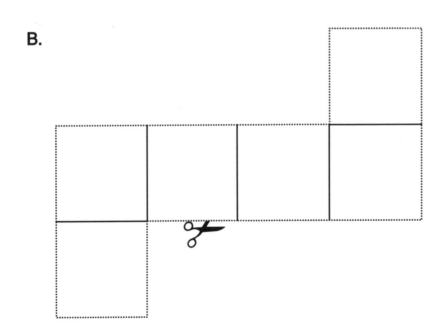

B.

Student Guide

Questions 1–7 (SG pp. 256–260)

1. 6 faces
2. 12 edges
3. 8 vertices
4. Answers will vary.
5. *Answers will vary.
6. Answers will vary.
7. 7 faces, 15 edges, 10 vertices

Homework (SG pp. 260–262)

Questions 1–12

1. Answers will vary.
2. no
3. no
4. no
5. yes
6. prism, rectangular bases, 6 faces
7. not a prism, 4 faces
8. prism, triangular bases, 5 faces
9. prism, pentagonal bases, 7 faces
10. not a prism, 5 faces
11. prism, pentagonal bases, 7 faces
12. not a prism, 14 faces

Discovery Assignment Book

**Home Practice (DAB p. 125)

Part 4. Time

Questions 1–2

1. **A.** 8:00   **B.** 10:25
   C. 4:40   **D.** 11:12
   E. 3:28   **F.** 2:53
2. **A.** 8:15 P.M.   **B.** 8:45 A.M.
   C. 8:40 P.M.   **D.** 3:55 P.M.
   E. 155 min.   **F.** 10 hours

Nets (DAB pp. 141–143)

Questions 1–6

1. yes   2. no
3. no   4. no
5. yes   6. no

A Hexagonal Prism (DAB p. 145)

Questions 1–6

1. 120°   2. 2 cm
3. 10 cm   4. G
5. H   6. J

*Answers and/or discussion are included in the Lesson Guide.
**Answers for all the Home Practice in the *Discovery Assignment Book* are at the end of the unit.

0. Multiplying by
   Multiples of Ten (URG p. 21)

A. $8 \times 500 =$ B. $6 \times 100 =$

C. $2 \times 5000 =$ D. $5000 \times 6 =$

E. $50,000 \times 1 =$ F. $9 \times 50 =$

Q. Measuring Volume (URG p. 22)

Maya filled a 250-cc graduated cylinder with 140 cc of water. She added four marbles to the cylinder. The water level rose to 156 cc.

1. What is the total volume of the marbles?

2. What is the volume of one of the marbles?

3. Maya predicted that the total volume of the four marbles was 19 cc. Was her prediction within 10% of the actual volume of the four marbles?

DPP Task and Challenge are on page 93. Suggestions for using the DPPs are on page 93.

LESSON GUIDE 6

Finding the Volume of a Prism

Estimated Class Sessions: 2–3

The volume of a rectangular prism is defined as the number of unit cubes needed to fill (or build) the shape. Volume is measured by finding the area of the base and then multiplying by the number of cube layers needed to build the height. The notion of volume is generalized for other prisms as well. In an optional part of the lesson, students connect this new method for finding the volume of a prism to finding volume by displacement.

Key Content

- Finding the volume of prisms.
- Measuring area in square centimeters.
- Measuring length (height) in centimeters.

Curriculum Sequence

Before This Unit

Volume. In Grade 3 Unit 16, students built models of small objects using centimeter connecting cubes and estimated the volume of the objects by counting the cubes in their models. Then, they placed the actual objects in a graduated cylinder and measured the volume by displacement. In Grade 3 Unit 18, students found the height, area of the base, and volume of cube models. In Unit 20, they found the volume of prisms built with centimeter connecting cubes.

In Grade 4 Unit 8, students found the volume of objects by displacement using graduated cylinders. Volume was defined, and the appropriate units used to measure volume were discussed.

Materials List

Print Materials for Students

	Math Facts and Daily Practice and Problems	Activity	Homework	Written Assessment
Student Books — Student Guide		*Finding the Volume of a Prism* Pages 263–266	*Finding the Volume of a Prism* Homework Section Pages 266–267	
Discovery Assignment Book				Home Practice Part 5 Page 126
Teacher Resources — Facts Resource Guide	DPP Items 9O & 9R			
Unit Resource Guide	DPP Items O–R Pages 21–23			
Generic Section		*Centimeter Grid Paper,* 2–3 per student		

available on Teacher Resource CD

All Transparency Masters, Blackline Masters, and Assessment Blackline Masters in the Unit Resource Guide are on the Teacher Resource CD.

Supplies for Each Student Group

75 centimeter connecting cubes
right triangular prism (made from nets in Lesson 5)
250-cc graduated cylinder, optional
paper towels, optional
set of geometric wooden solids or assortment of prisms with different shapes as bases
various prisms small enough to fit into the graduated cylinder, optional

juice pack (250 ml) or half pint milk carton
calculators
eyedropper, optional
small container for water, optional

Materials for the Teacher

Transparency of *Centimeter Grid Paper* (Unit Resource Guide, Generic Section)
Observational Assessment Record (Unit Resource Guide, Pages 9–10 and Teacher Resource CD)
Individual Assessment Record Sheet (Teacher Implementation Guide, Assessment section and Teacher Resource CD)
base-ten pack
10 base-ten flats
approximately 75 centimeter connecting cubes
right rectangular prism (made from the net in Lesson 5)
250-cc graduated cylinder for demonstration, optional
various prisms small enough to fit into the graduated cylinder, optional
eyedropper, optional
container for water, optional

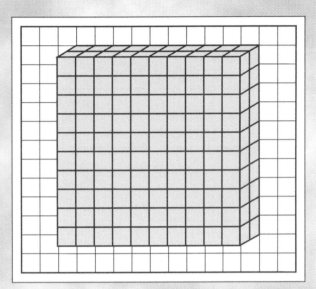

Figure 43: *Building a pack with layers of flats*

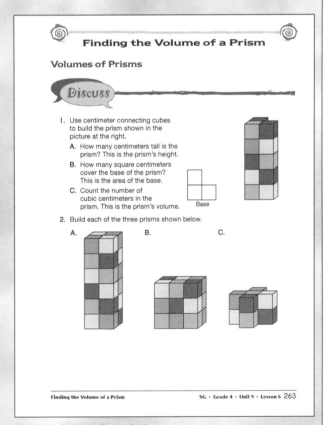

Student Guide - Page 263

Before the Activity

Collect juice boxes to be used while completing the Juice Box Volume section on the *Finding the Volume of a Prism* Activity Pages in the *Student Guide.* You may substitute half-pint milk cartons if necessary. (See the TIMS Tip in Part 2 of the Lesson Guide.)

Developing the Activity

Part 1. Volumes of Prisms

Begin with a transparency of *Centimeter Grid Paper* and a base-ten pack. Demonstrate tracing one face of the pack on the *Centimeter Grid Paper* on the overhead projector. Make sure students see that you have traced around 100 square centimeters. This is the area of a face of the cube.

Remind students that **volume** is the space an object takes up. We often measure volume in cubic centimeters. Now, ask students to imagine that you could cut off the top face and open up the cube. If you have a cardboard pack, you can actually open a side. By questioning, review with your class the number of centimeter cubes that will fit inside the cube. Remind them of the work they did in Unit 8. Suggest thinking about layers of cubes. Demonstrate building the cube by placing flats atop the surface area outlined on the overhead projector as in Figure 43. Count by 100s as you lay the 10 flats down to make 1000 cc. Make sure students see the difference between square centimeters and cubic centimeters, i.e., the difference between area and volume.

Begin a discussion of the questions on the *Finding the Volume of a Prism* Activity Pages in the *Student Guide. Question 1* asks students to build a prism that has a base of 3 sq cm and a height of 5 cm as shown in Figure 44. Students must find the height in centimeters, the area of the base in square centimeters, and the volume in cubic centimeters. To help students find the area of the base, place a completed prism on a transparency of *Centimeter Grid Paper* and trace the base. Ask:

• *How many square centimeters are in the base?*

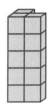

Figure 44: *Building a prism*

Prism	Area of Base in sq cm	Height in cm	Volume in cc
A	4 sq cm	6 cm	24 cc
B	6 sq cm	3 cm	18 cc
C	5 sq cm	2 cm	10 cc

Figure 45: *A completed table for **Question 3** in the* Student Guide

In **Questions 2–3,** students build three more prisms pictured in the *Student Guide* and record the area of the base, the height, and the volume in a table. A completed table is shown in Figure 45.

Question 4 asks students to use the information in the table to devise a method for finding the volume of a prism. Students should see that multiplying the area of the base times the height will give the volume of each prism in the table. Relate the multiplication sentences (i.e., 4 sq cm × 6 cm = 24 cc) to multiplying the area of the base times the number of layers of cubes needed to build the prism.

Question 5 extends this idea to the volume of prisms (boxes) that cannot be made with centimeter connecting cubes. Students find the volume of a triangular prism. The base is shown on grid paper so that students can find the area by counting square centimeters. The area of the base of the triangle is 2 sq cm, the height is given as 10 cm, so the volume of the box is 2 sq cm × 10 cm = 20 cc. Explain to students that most objects do not have dimensions that are whole centimeters. When we talk about the volume of a solid being some number of cubic centimeters, the cubes are not necessarily whole cubes.

TIMS Tip

The prisms are easier to build if students do not try to connect the layers. Building layers and then laying the layers on top of one another also reinforces the notion that volume can be found by finding the area of the base and then counting the layers of cubes that fit this area.

---

3. Copy the data table on a piece of paper. Find the area of the base, the height, and the volume of each of the prisms in Question 2. Complete the table.

Prism	Area of Base in sq cm	Height in cm	Volume in cc
A			
B			
C			

4. A. Look at the information in the table. Describe any patterns you see.
   B. Describe a method for finding the volume of a prism without counting cubes.
   C. Check your method. Use it to find the volume of the prism in Question 1. Did you find the same volume using your new method as you did when you counted cubes?

One way to think about volume is to ask how many cubes (or parts of cubes) fit into the object.

5. Jackie got a box of chocolates for her birthday. The box is a triangular prism.

264 SG · Grade 4 · Unit 9 · Lesson 6   Finding the Volume of a Prism

Student Guide - Page 264

A. Jackie traced the base of the box on a piece of *Centimeter Grid Paper* as shown here. What is the area of the base?

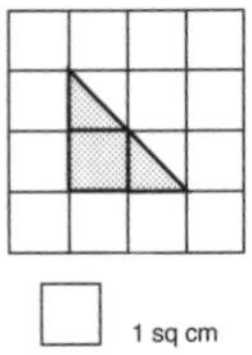

☐ 1 sq cm

B. The height (or length) of the box is 10 cm. Use your method for finding the volume of a prism to find the volume of Jackie's box.

Juice Box Volume

6. About how much is a ml of juice? A cupful, a spoonful, or less than a spoonful? (Remember, 1 ml = 1 cc.)

7. Is your juice box a prism?

8. Find the volume of your juice box. Explain the steps you used. Give the volume of your juice box in ml.

9. Look at the label of your juice box. Was the volume you calculated close to the volume printed on the box? Explain.

Finding the Volume of a Prism   SG · Grade 4 · Unit 9 · Lesson 6   265

Student Guide - Page 265

Part 2. Juice Box Volume

Students read the Juice Box Volume section in the *Student Guide* and complete **Questions 6–9.** Distribute juice boxes to the students. Through class participation and discussion, help students understand that one way of finding the volume of the juice box is again to begin with the area of the base. Most juice boxes will not have dimensions that are whole centimeters. Stress to students that the best they can do is find a good estimate. You will need to approximate the area by tracing the base of the box on *Centimeter Grid Paper* and counting square centimeters. One way to approximate the area is by matching squares. That is, count all the complete squares first. Then try to match incomplete squares to make whole squares as shown in Figure 46.

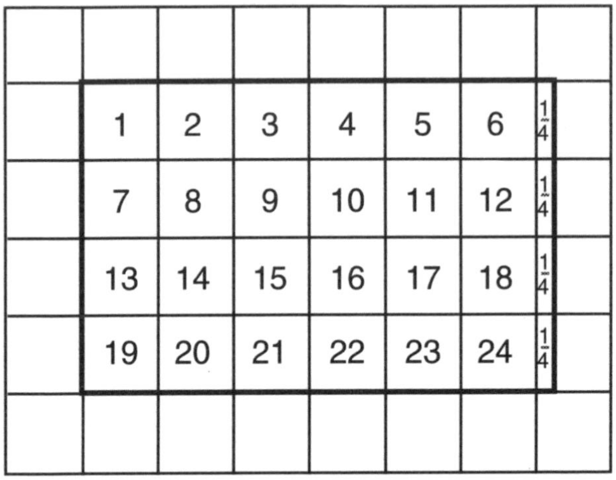

	1	2	3	4	5	6	¼
	7	8	9	10	11	12	¼
	13	14	15	16	17	18	¼
	19	20	21	22	23	24	¼

Area = 25 sq cm

Figure 46: *Finding the area of the base of a juice box*

Ask:

• *How can you find the volume of the box, now that you know the area of the base? This means finding how many centimeter cubes are needed to fill the box completely. Or, how many centimeter cubes are needed to build a replica of the box?*

Discuss how to approach the problem with the class. Some students may suggest building an approximate replica of the box story-by-story, just as the flats can be used to build a pack. Other students may suggest building a single tower up, and then multiplying the area of the base by the number of layers they find will fit. A third, more abstract way is to find the number of layers of cubes that will fit by measuring with a ruler. Make sure your students see all three ways.

A 250-ml juice box has dimensions (approximately) 6 cm × 4 cm × 10.5 cm, yielding a volume of 252 cc. This is very close to the volume given on most boxes, 250 ml. If students find the area of the base by counting square centimeters, measure the height to the nearest centimeter, and then multiply the area of the base times the height, the volume calculated by the students will likely be close to the volume printed on the box. As a final exercise, you can open one of the juice boxes and pour it into a 250-cc graduated cylinder to check how accurate the manufacturers are in filling the boxes.

Question 10 asks students to use the same method they used to find the volume of the juice box to find the volume of the right triangular prism they built from nets in Lesson 5. Students can trace the base of their prisms on grid paper to find the base area. See Figure 47. Then, the volume can be found by multiplying the area of the base by the height. Use ***Question 11*** as a check to see if students can complete the homework on their own. The homework section includes similar problems.

TIMS Tip
If you do not collect enough juice boxes, half pint (236 ml) milk cartons from the school lunchroom can be used as well. Cut off the pointed top so that an open box with rectangular sides remains. Students should follow the same procedure as described for the juice box. Note: Many other products sold in boxes are sold by weight, not volume, and would not be appropriate for this particular activity.

Area of base is 8 sq cm.
Height of right triangular prism is 7 cm.
Volume = 8 sq cm × 7 cm = 56 cc

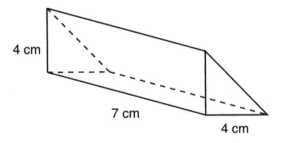

Figure 47: *Finding the volume of the right triangular prism from Lesson 5*

Part 3. Volume by Displacement (optional)

In this unit, volume was investigated by measuring the area of the base and the height. In Unit 8, the volume of an object was measured by finding the amount of water the object displaced in a graduated cylinder. Students can connect the two methods by finding the volume of prisms that will fit into a 250-cc graduated cylinder using both procedures. This will help students see the relationship between 1 cc and 1 ml and gain a better understanding of the concept of volume. Also, it stresses a theme that runs throughout the curriculum; that there are often many ways to solve a problem in mathematics.

They may use prisms from a set of geometric solids or other prisms such as small plastic boxes. Each group will also need *Centimeter Grid Paper,* a ruler, a calculator, a 250-cc graduated cylinder, a small container for water, an eyedropper, and paper towels. First, they find the volume of a prism by estimating the area of the base, measuring the height, and multiplying the two measurements. Then, they find the volume of the same prism by displacement.

Journal Prompt
Write a letter to a friend describing how to find the volume of a box. You may use a specific example, if you wish.

Suggestions for Teaching the Lesson

Math Facts

DPP Bit O practices multiplication by multiples of 10. Task R provides fact practice using fact families.

Homework and Practice

- Assign the questions in the Homework section in the *Student Guide*. Students may need calculators for some of the multiplication.
- DPP Challenge P offers a geometry puzzle in which students find the number of squares, the number of triangles, and the lines of symmetry in a Latvian design. Bit Q reviews measuring volume by displacement.

Volumes of other prisms can be found using the same method: Find the area of the base and then multiply by the height.

10. Find the volume of the right triangular prism you built in Lesson 5.

11. A. What is the area of the base of the prism shown in the picture below?
    B. What is the volume of the prism?

Homework
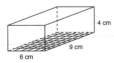

For Questions 1–4, a picture of a box is shown for each problem. Find the volume of the box. You can use a calculator to help you multiply.

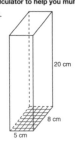

1.

2.

Student Guide - Page 266

P. Challenge: Latvian Puzzzle
(URG p. 22)

1. Count the number of squares in the design.

2. Count the number of triangles in the design.

3. Draw as many lines of symmetry as you can in the design.

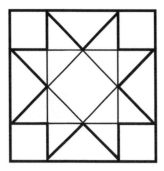

R. Task: Even More Fact Families for × and ÷ (URG p. 23)

The following four facts are in the same fact family:

$6 \times 5 = 30$ $\quad$ $5 \times 6 = 30$

$30 \div 5 = 6$ $\quad$ $30 \div 6 = 5$

Solve each pair of related number sentences.

Then, give two other facts that are in the same fact family.

A. $2 \times 10 = ?$ and $20 \div 10 = ?$

B. $3 \times 5 = ?$ and $15 \div 5 = ?$

C. $7 \times 5 = ?$ and $35 \div 7 = ?$

D. $10 \times 9 = ?$ and $90 \div 9 = ?$

E. $4 \times 10 = ?$ and $40 \div 10 = ?$

F. $5 \times 9 = ?$ and $45 \div 9 = ?$

3. The area of the triangular base of this prism is 15 sq cm.

11 cm

4. The area of the hexagonal base of this prism is about 26 sq cm.

6 cm

5. Ana found that the area of the bottom (the base) of her purse is 90 sq cm. To find the volume, she measured the height of her purse. It is 15 cm tall. What is the volume of Ana's purse?

Student Guide - Page 267

Name_____ Date _____

Part 5 Geometry

You will need a protractor, a ruler, and two pieces of *Centimeter Grid Paper* to complete this part of the Home Practice.

1. Nicholas built the prism at the right from centimeter connecting cubes.
   A. How many centimeters tall is the prism?
   B. How many square centimeters cover the base of the prism?
   C. What is the volume of the prism?

2. What is the volume of each of the prisms below? Show how you found your answer.

   A.   B. The area of the base is 56 sq cm.

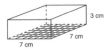

   3 cm

   7 cm

   7 cm

   3 cm

3. Draw each of the angles described below with a ruler and protractor on a separate sheet of paper.
   A. Draw a 35° angle. Name the angle ∠QRT.
   B. Draw a 142° angle. Name the angle ∠XYZ.

4. Go to a cupboard (ask an adult first). Select three objects that are prisms (boxes) such as a gelatin box, a small cereal box, and a toothpaste box.
   A. Estimate the volume in cubic centimeters of each box.
   B. Trace the base of each on *Centimeter Grid Paper*. How many sq cm cover the base of each box?
   C. Measure the height of each box in cm.
   D. Use the information you gathered in 4B and 4C to find the volume of each container. Were your estimates close to your answers?

Discovery Assignment Book - Page 126

Suggestions for Teaching the Lesson (continued)

Assessment

- Use **Questions 1–3** of Part 5 of the Home Practice in the *Discovery Assignment Book* as an assessment.

- Observe students as they find the volume of prisms using different strategies. Record your observations on the *Observational Assessment Record*.

- Transfer appropriate documentation from the Unit 9 *Observational Assessment Record* to the students' *Individual Assessment Record Sheets*.

Answers for Part 5 of the Home Practice can be found at the end of this lesson and the end of this unit.

Extension

Use **Question 4** of Home Practice Part 5 as an extension. Students estimate the volume of boxes from the kitchen at home. Then, they measure the volume to check their estimates.

AT A GLANCE

Math Facts and Daily Practice and Problems

DPP items O and R provide practice with multiplication and division facts. Challenge P presents a geometric puzzle. Bit Q reviews measuring volume by displacement.

Part 1. Volumes of Prisms

1. Find the area of a face of a base-ten pack on *Centimeter Grid Paper.* (100 sq cm)
2. Discuss volume as filling an object with cm cubes or building the object with cubes.
3. Demonstrate building base-ten packs by layering flats made up of 100 cm cubes. Find the volume of the pack by counting the layers, skip counting by 100s, from 100 cc to 1000 cc.
4. Students complete *Questions 1–5* on the *Finding the Volume of a Prism* Activity Pages in the *Student Guide.*

Part 2. Juice Box Volume

1. Student groups find the volume of a juice box by completing the Juice Box Volume section in the *Student Guide (Questions 6–9).*
2. Students find the volume of the right triangular prisms they made from nets in Lesson 5 in *Question 10.*
3. Check to see that students are ready to complete the homework independently by completing *Question 11.*

Part 3. Volume by Displacement (optional)

1. Students find the volume of prisms small enough to fit inside 250 cc graduated cylinders by multiplying the area of the base by the height.
2. Students find the volumes of the same prisms by displacement and compare the two ways to measure volume.

Homework

Assign the Homework section in the *Student Guide.*

Assessment

1. Use *Questions 1–3* of Home Practice Part 5 as an assessment.
2. Use the *Observational Assessment Record* to document students' abilities to measure the volume of a prism.
3. Transfer appropriate documentation from the Unit 9 *Observational Assessment Record* to students' *Individual Assessment Record Sheets.*

Notes:

Student Guide

Questions 1–11 (SG pp. 263–266)

1. **A.** 5 cm

   B. 3 sq cm

   C. 15 cc

2. Students build prisms.

3.

Prism	Area of Base in sq cm	Height in cm	Volume in cc
A	4 sq cm	6 cm	24 cc
B	6 sq cm	3 cm	18 cc
C	5 sq cm	2 cm	10 cc

4. **A.** Answers will vary. One possible pattern is that the area of the base times the height gives the volume.

   B. Multiply the area of the base by the height.

   C. Answers will vary.

5. **A.** 2 sq cm

   B. 20 cc

6. less than a spoonful

7. yes

8. *Answers will vary. A 250-ml juice box is approximately 6 cm by 4 cm by 10.5 cm yielding a volume of 252 cc.

9. *Answers will vary.

10. *56 cc; See Figure 47 in Lesson Guide 6.

11. **A.** 54 sq cm

    B. 216 cc

Homework (SG pp. 266–267)

Questions 1–5

1. 125 cc

2. 800 cc

3. 165 cc

4. 156 cc

5. 1350 cc

Discovery Assignment Book

**Home Practice (DAB p. 126)

Part 5. Geometry

Questions 1–4

1. **A.** 4 cm

   B. 9 sq cm

   C. 36 cc

2. **A.** 147 cc; 49 sq cm × 3 cm = 147 cc

   B. 168 cc; 56 sq cm × 3 cm = 168 cc

3. **A.**

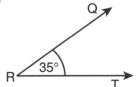

   B.

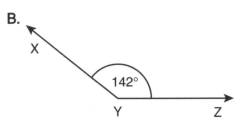

4. Answers will vary.

---

*Answers and/or discussion are included in the Lesson Guide.

**Answers for all the Home Practice in the *Discovery Assignment Book* are at the end of the unit.

Building an Octahedron

OPTIONAL LESSON

Estimated Class Sessions: 1

Students construct an octahedron and discuss the mathematics they see. The octahedron can be decorated and displayed. This optional activity can be completed any time after Lesson 5 and can be combined with art class.

There are no Daily Practice and Problems items for this lesson.

Key Content

- Constructing a geometric solid.
- Identifying faces, edges, and vertices of a solid.
- Describing a regular solid.

Key Vocabulary

face
octahedron
regular solid

Materials List

Print Materials for Students

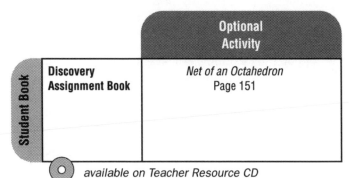

Student Book

	Optional Activity
Discovery Assignment Book	*Net of an Octahedron* Page 151

○ *available on Teacher Resource CD*

All Transparency Masters, Blackline Masters, and Assessment Blackline Masters in the Unit Resource Guide are on the Teacher Resource CD.

Supplies for Each Student

tape
scissors
string, optional

Materials for the Teacher

Net of an Octahedron Activity Page (Discovery Assignment Book) Page 151
tape
scissors

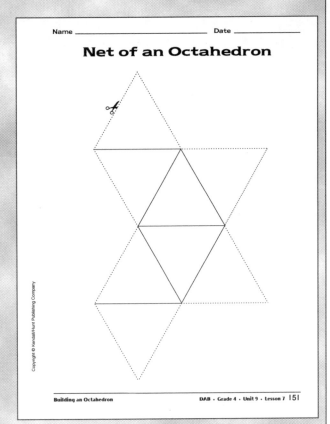

Net of an Octahedron

Building an Octahedron   DAB · Grade 4 · Unit 9 · Lesson 7   151

Discovery Assignment Book - Page 151

𝕋IMS Tip

You may want to make copies of the *Net of an Octahedron* Activity Page onto cardstock to make it easier for students to fold.

📓 Journal Prompt

Write a letter to a friend describing the solid you made in class. Use the terms: faces, edges, vertices.

Developing the Activity

Many children enjoy building models. The net provided here builds an octahedron. The octahedron is composed of eight equilateral triangles. Four triangles meet at each vertex of the octahedron.

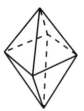

Figure 48: *An octahedron*

Discuss the mathematics of the solid that students are constructing. For example, the faces of the octahedron are eight identical equilateral triangles. This means that each triangle has all sides equal in length and all angles have equal measure (60°). Discuss the symmetries found in the triangle. Students should recognize that the figure is not a prism.

Have children cut out the net carefully. They can decorate the net before folding it into an octahedron. Then, students should score the interior lines with a ruler and sharp pencil. Have students use tape to connect the edges of the octahedron's net. A string or wire for hanging can be inserted before the final closure.

Discuss the solids after they are completed. Focus children's attention on the regularity of the solid. Note that four triangles meet at each vertex of the octahedron. Use the words face, edge, vertex, equilateral triangle, octahedron, etc.

These make wonderful classroom or hall decorations and show children a connection between mathematics and art.

Developing the Activity

1. Students use the *Net of an Octahedron* Activity Page from the *Discovery Assignment Book* to make an octahedron.
2. Discuss the net.
3. Students cut out the net and decorate it.
4. Students score the interior lines before folding the net.
5. Students tape the edges of the net together. A string or wire for hanging can be inserted before the final closure.
6. Discuss the solid: faces, edges, vertices.

Notes:

S. Add, Subtract, and Multiply

(URG p. 23)

Solve the following problems using paper and pencil or mental math. Be sure to estimate to see if your answers are reasonable.

1. A. $7980 + 345 =$ B. $60 \times 500 =$

    C. $4021 - 765 =$ D. $3000 - 462 =$

    E. $42 \times 9 =$ F. $38 \times 5 =$

2. Explain your strategy for Question 1D.

U. Quiz: 5s and 10s (URG p. 25)

A. $30 \div 3 =$ B. $10 \div 1 =$

C. $10 \div 2 =$ D. $60 \div 10 =$

E. $40 \div 8 =$ F. $5 \div 5 =$

G. $20 \div 5 =$ H. $80 \div 10 =$

I. $30 \div 6 =$ J. $35 \div 5 =$

K. $15 \div 3 =$ L. $50 \div 10 =$

M. $70 \div 10 =$ N. $90 \div 9 =$

O. $40 \div 4 =$ P. $20 \div 2 =$

Q. $100 \div 10 =$ R. $25 \div 5 =$

S. $45 \div 5 =$

DPP Task and Challenge are on page 103.
Suggestions for using the DPPs are on page 103.

LESSON GUIDE

Constructing a Prism

Estimated Class Sessions: 2

Most of the main concepts of this unit are involved in this assessment lesson. Part 1 involves measuring angles and finding turn and line symmetry. In Part 2, students demonstrate understanding of nets and prisms.

Key Content

*   Measuring angles with a protractor.
*   Identifying turn and line symmetries.
*   Constructing a net.

Materials List

Print Materials for Students

	Math Facts and Daily Practice and Problems	Assessment Activity	Written Assessment
Facts Resource Guide ⊙	DPP Items 9U & 9V		DPP Item 9U *Quiz: 5s and 10s*
Unit Resource Guide	DPP Items S–V Pages 23–25 ⊙		DPP Item U *Quiz: 5s and 10s* Page 25 ⊙ and *Constructing a Prism* Page 105
Generic Section ⊙		*Centimeter Grid Paper,* 1 per student	

Teacher Resources

⊙ *available on Teacher Resource CD*

All Transparency Masters, Blackline Masters, and Assessment Blackline Masters in the Unit Resource Guide are on the Teacher Resource CD.

Supplies for Each Student Group

rulers
protractors
scissors
tape
calculators

Materials for the Teacher

TIMS Multidimensional Rubric (Teacher Implementation Guide, Assessment section), optional

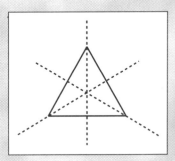

Figure 49: *Lines of symmetry*

Developing the Activity

Students complete the *Constructing a Prism* Assessment Blackline Master.

Part 1. Symmetries

Part 1 can be completed after Lesson 3. In **Question 1,** the angles of the equilateral triangle are 60°. Answers between 58° and 62° should be accepted.

In **Question 2,** there are three lines of symmetry as sketched in Figure 49. Students should be accurate in finding the midpoints of the sides either by measuring or by folding. Students should draw the lines with a straightedge.

In **Question 3,** the triangle has $\frac{1}{3}$-turn symmetry

In **Question 4,** the angle of turning is 120° since $\frac{360}{3} = 120$.

Part 2. Making a Prism

In this section, use your professional judgment as to how much guidance to give students. We suggest students be allowed to work in groups to design the net in **Question 5.** Students should each have their own copy of the net to complete the assessment.

In **Question 5,** the length of the rectangles is not specified in the problem, making it a more of an open-response question. The size of the net is constricted by the size of a sheet of grid paper (unless they want to paste pages together). If a group has trouble getting started, encourage them to think and discuss first. Ask:

- *Look at the net of the hexagonal prism you constructed in Lesson 5.*
- *What will a triangular prism look like? What shape are the bases? What shape are the sides?*
- *How many rectangles will be needed for the faces of the prism?*
- *What must be the width of the rectangular faces?*
- *You can choose the length of the rectangular faces.*

You can use the Solving dimension of the *TIMS Multidimensional Rubric* to score their work.

Solutions will vary to **Question 5.** Lengths of the rectangles will vary. Students should have constructed the net so that the widths of the rectangles are 5 cm (the length of the side of the triangle). The two triangles can be attached to any of the rectangles.

Suggestions for Teaching the Lesson

Math Facts

DPP Challenge V is a set of riddles that uses math facts.

Homework and Practice

DPP Bit S provides practice with addition, subtraction, and multiplication. Task T asks students to read a train schedule and solve problems involving elapsed time.

Assessment

DPP Bit U is a quiz on the division facts for the fives and tens.

Daily Practice and Problems:
Task & Challenge for Lesson 8

T. Task: All Aboard! (URG p. 24)

Answer the questions below using the following train schedule.

Leaving Chicago—Going to Roselle					
Chicago	8:30 AM	10:30 AM	12:30 PM	2:30 PM	4:30 PM
Oak Park	8:50 AM	10:50 AM	12:50 PM	2:50 PM	4:50 PM
Itasca	9:03 AM	11:03 AM	1:03 PM	3:03 PM	5:03 PM
Roselle	9:37 AM	11:37 AM	1:37 PM	3:37 PM	5:37 PM

1. Lee Yah and her sister are catching the 12:30 P.M. train in Chicago. At what time will they arrive in Roselle?

2. Irma's mother needs to arrive in Roselle before 4:00 P.M. What is the last train she can take leaving from Chicago?

3. The 8:30 A.M. train from Chicago is delayed 8 minutes. At what time will it arrive in Itasca?

4. Linda and her cousin took the 10:50 A.M. train from Oak Park to Roselle. How long was the train ride?

V. Challenge: Who Am I?
   (URG p. 25)

Answer each riddle below.

1. I am three less than five squared.

2. I am two times as great as the sum of five and eight.

3. I am half the difference of ten and four.

4. I am six more than the product of nine and three.

5. If you subtract the product of four and three from the sum of eleven and four, you will know who I am.

6. Make up your own riddle to share.

AT A GLANCE

Math Facts and Daily Practice and Problems

DPP item S practices computation. Task T works with time. Bit U is a quiz on the division facts for the fives and tens. Challenge V contains riddles that develop number sense.

Part 1. Symmetries

Students complete Part 1 of the *Constructing a Prism* Assessment Blackline Master.

Part 2. Making a Prism

Students complete Part 2 of the *Constructing a Prism* Assessment Blackline Master. Provide assistance as needed.

Assessment

1. Use DPP item U *Quiz: 5s and 10s* to assess students' fluency with the division facts in these groups.
2. Score students' work on Part 2 using the Solving dimension of the *TIMS Multidimensional Rubric.*

Notes:

Constructing a Prism

You may use scissors, a ruler, a protractor, a calculator, and tape to complete Questions 1–5.

Part 1. Symmetries

1. Find the angle measures of the triangle. Label them on the triangle.

2. Using a straightedge, draw all the lines of symmetry for the triangle. Be as accurate as you can. You may cut out one of the triangles at the bottom of the page and fold it if you wish.

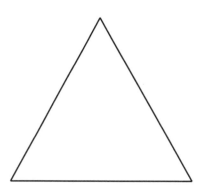

Another copy of the same triangle is provided at the bottom of the page to answer Questions 3 and 4. The center is marked.

3. Find the type of turn symmetry for the triangle.

4. Find the angle of turning for the triangle.

Part 2. Making a Prism

5. Make a net of a triangular prism using the given triangle as a base. Use a sheet of *Centimeter Grid Paper.*

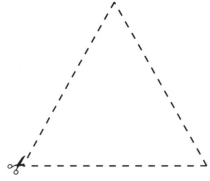

You may use this triangle for Question 1.

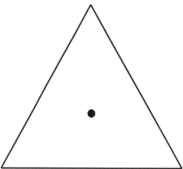

You may use this triangle for Questions 3 and 4.

Unit Resource Guide

Constructing a Prism (URG p. 105)

Questions 1–5

1. *Each angle measures 60°. Accept answers between 58° and 62°.

2. *

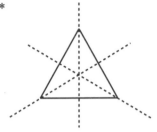

3. $\frac{1}{3}$-turn symmetry

4. *120°

5. There are many solutions. Two possible solutions follow. Lengths of the rectangles will vary.

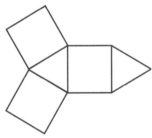

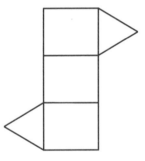

---

*Answers and/or discussion are included in the Lesson Guide.

**Answers for all the Home Practice in the *Discovery Assignment Book* are at the end of the unit.

Discovery Assignment Book

Home Practice

Part 2. Mental Multiplication

Questions 1–3 (DAB p. 123)

1. **A.** 60,000
   B. 35,000
   C. 3600
   D. 45,000
   E. 80,000
   F. 25,000
2. **A.** $4.80
   B. $14
   C. about $3.50
3. **A.** 65¢
   B. $1.05
   C. $2.10

Part 3. Addition, Subtraction, and Multiplication

Questions 1–3 (DAB p. 124)

1. **A.** 423
   B. 38
   C. 3001
   D. 1260
   E. 7648
   F. 1544
2. Answers will vary. Possible answers include:
   A. $300 \times 20 = 6000$
   B. $500 \times 60 = 30,000$
   C. $10,000 \times 9 = 90,000$
3. **A.** 252
   B. 296
   C. 252
   D. 336
   E. 198
   F. 432

Part 4. Time

Questions 1–2 (DAB p. 125)

1. **A.** 8:00
   B. 10:25
   C. 4:40
   D. 11:12
   E. 3:28
   F. 2:53
2. **A.** 8:15 P.M.
   B. 8:45 A.M.
   C. 8:40 P.M.
   D. 3:55 P.M.
   E. 155 min.
   F. 10 hours

Part 5. Geometry

Questions 1–4 (DAB p. 126)

1. **A.** 4 cm
   B. 9 sq cm
   C. 36 cc
2. **A.** 147 cc; 49 sq cm $\times$ 3 cm = 147 cc
   B. 168 cc; 56 sq cm $\times$ 3 cm = 168 cc
3. **A.**

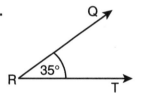

   B.

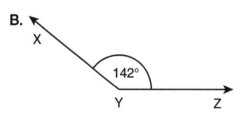

4. Answers will vary.

---

*Answers and/or discussion are included in the Lesson Guide.